THE
TECHNIQUE
OF THE
GREAT PAINTERS

Processes, Pigments, and Vehicles—a Manual for Art Students, 1895.

Greek and Roman Methods of Painting, 1910.

Materials used in the Painter's Craft, from the Earliest Times to the End of the 17th Century, 1911.

The Pigments and Mediums of the Old Masters, 1914.

The Painter's Methods and Materials, 1926.

A Study of Rembrandt, and His School, 1929.

The Brushwork of Rembrandt and his School, 1932.

Simple Rules for Painting in Oils, 1934.

New Light on Old Masters, 1935.

INITIAL LETTER FROM THE LINDISFARNE GOSPEL

Circa A.D. *100*   *British Museum*

THE
TECHNIQUE
OF THE
GREAT PAINTERS

by

A. P. LAURIE

M.A. (Cantab.), D.Sc., LL.D. (Edin.), F.R.S.E., F.C.S.
Sometime Professor of Chemistry to
The Royal Academy of Arts

LONDON
CARROLL AND NICHOLSON LTD
MCMXLIX

Printed and made in Great Britain by
HAGUE AND GILL
at Pigotts, near High Wycombe, Buckinghamshire

and published by
CARROLL AND NICHOLSON LTD.
at Tudor House, 1 Princeton Street, Bedford Row,
London, W.C. 1

M C M X L I X

DEDICATION

I HAVE much pleasure in dedicating this book to my friend Professor Edward W. Forbes of Harvard University, who has done so much to advance our knowledge of the technical methods of the Old Masters.

A. P. LAURIE.

CONTENTS

	Foreword	13
CHAPTER I	Painting in Egypt, Greece, and Rome	23
CHAPTER II	Buon Fresco in Classical Times	35
CHAPTER III	Buon Fresco	41
CHAPTER IV	Mediæval Pigments	49
CHAPTER V	Pigments described by Cennino Cennini	63
CHAPTER VI	Painting with Yolk of Egg	79
CHAPTER VII	Painting in Drying Oil	87
CHAPTER VIII	The Building-up of a Painting in the Fourteenth and Fifteenth Centuries	103
CHAPTER IX	Light	115
CHAPTER X	The Rokeby Venus	121
CHAPTER XI	Brushwork	125
CHAPTER XII	Mediæval Varnishes	155
CHAPTER XIII	The Persian Illuminated MSS.	159
CHAPTER XIV	Forgeries	175
CHAPTER XV	Emulsions and the Van Eyck Medium	187
	Index	191

LIST OF PLATES

Frontispiece   Initial letter from the Lindisfarne Gospel   *facing title page*

PLATE 1   Greco-Roman portrait from Hawara, in wax   *facing page*
           National Gallery 1265   34

PLATE 2   *Virgin and Child* by Andrea Mantegna. Carrara
           Gallery, Bergamo. Tempera, painted about 1460   78

PLATE 3   *Virgin and Child* by Hans Memling. Nelson Atkins
           Gallery, Kansas City. Oil, painted about 1460   86

PLATE 4   Portion of *Jan Arnolfini and his Wife* by Jan Van Eyck,
           a perfect example of Stand Oil technique
           National Gallery 186   92

PLATE 5   *The Bird Trap* by Pieter Breughel the Elder   102

PLATE 6   *Santa Barbara*, unfinished picture by Jan Van Eyck
           Antwerp Museum   108

PLATE 7   *Madonna Enthroned*, unfinished picture by Cima da
           Conegliano. National Gallery of Scotland 1190   110

PLATE 8   *The Entombment*, unfinished picture by Michelangelo
           National Gallery 790   112

PLATE 9   *Madonna and Child*, unfinished picture by Michelangelo
           National Gallery 809   114

PLATE 10   *The Rokeby Venus* by Velazquez
           National Gallery 2057   120

PLATE 11   *Saskia Laughing* by Rembrandt
           Dresden Gallery   130

PLATE 12   Photomicrograph of the tassel on the shoulder from
           Saskia Laughing   132

PLATE 13   Photomicrograph of detail from *The Rape of Proserpine* by
           Rembrandt, showing modelling of leaves in white lead
           Kaiser Friedrich Museum, Berlin 823   134

PLATE 14   Identifying Rembrandt's brushwork by comparison
           with brushwork from *Woman Bathing*
           National Gallery 54   136

PLATE 15   *Man in Armour* by Carel Fabritius, with forged
Rembrandt signature. Cassel Gallery 245   138

PLATE 16   *Self Portrait* attributed to Rembrandt, signed and
dated. Kaiser Friedrich Museum, Berlin 810   140

PLATE 17   *Verdonck*, holding the jawbone of an ass,
by Frans Hals. National Gallery of Scotland 1200   142

PLATE 18   Detail from *Verdonck*: photomicrograph of moustache   144

PLATE 19   Detail from *Verdonck*: photomicrograph of eye   146

PLATE 20   Photomicrograph of hand, from *Portrait of a Lady*
by Frans Hals. National Gallery of Scotland   148

PLATE 21   Photomicrograph of bow from *Portrait of a Lady* by
Frans Hals   150

PLATE 22   *The Hon. Mrs Graham* by Thomas Gainsborough
National Gallery of Scotland 332   152

PLATE 23   *Lord Newton* by Sir Henry Raeburn. National Gallery
of Scotland 522   154

PLATE 24   Travelling microscope on horizontal bar with camera   168

PLATE 25   Ultra-violet lantern   170

PLATE 26   Ultra-violet photograph of picture retouched by
restorer   172

PLATE 27   A forged Hobbema signature   174

List of Illustrations in Text

FIGURE 1   Graph showing dates of use of various pigments   62

FIGURE 2   The brushes used by sign writers (actual size) from
Winsor & Newton's catalogue   95

FIGURE 3   Copy of the Van Eyck signature, by a signwriter,
painted with lamp black ground in stand oil   95

FIGURE 4   Graph of the rise in refractive index of linseed oil
with time of exposure   180

PREFACE

IT GIVES ME pleasure to write a short preface to this new work of Professor A. P. Laurie. He is too well known to need an introduction, but at the same time a word of gratitude may be in order to the man whose valuable studies in the field of the technique of painting have been a help and an inspiration to so many of us.

Professor Laurie feels that now is the moment to gather together the threads of his long and penetrating researches, which have been in one form or another published since as early as 1895.

Artists, professors of art, and museum officials are becoming increasingly aware of the importance of studying materials and methods of painting and their history, and it is to be hoped that the many admirers of Professor Laurie will find new values in this volume.

EDWARD W. FORBES

Fogg Museum of Art, Harvard University, Cambridge, Massachusetts

Dedication of The Book of the Art *by Cennino Cennini*

THE BOOK OF THE ART

MADE AND COMPOSED BY CENNINO DA COLLE

IN THE REVERENCE OF GOD

AND OF THE VIRGIN MARY

AND OF ST EUSTACHIUS AND OF ST FRANCIS

AND OF ST JOHN THE BAPTIST

AND OF ST ANTHONY OF PADUA

AND GENERALLY

OF ALL THE SAINTS OF GOD

AND IN THE REVERENCE OF GIOTTO

OF TADDIO

AND OF AGNOLO THE MASTER OF CENNINO

AND FOR THE

UTILITY AND GOOD AND ADVANTAGE

OF THOSE WHO WOULD ATTAIN

PERFECTION IN THE ART

FOREWORD

WHILE the Roman Empire was breaking up in the West, it continued to exist in the East until the Mohammedan conquest, and this period saw the rise and development of Byzantine art. Nor were the sister arts and sciences necessarily stagnant. The discoveries of the alchemists of Alexandria became the inheritance of their Mohammedan conquerors, and under the Arabs learning and civilisation rapidly progressed and schools were established at Baghdad, Alexandria, Cairo and Cordova. Charlemagne had not neglected the decoration of the Cathedrals, and in the quiet monasteries of Ireland, far removed from the turmoils of Europe, the monks were bringing to perfection the art of illuminating manuscripts. Moreover, the learned monastic orders were everywhere growing stronger from year to year, and bringing together all the knowledge of the past under the shadow of the Church; and the eleventh century had seen the rise of the universities, true children of the classical schools of philosophy.

The first MSS., therefore, which we shall have to consider come to us from the monasteries, where every craft was practised by the monks for the glory of God. For, besides the pursuit of agriculture and other useful crafts, the monks devoted themselves more especially to the artistic crafts, in order that the House of God might be richly embellished, and the people taught the truths of Christianity and the lives of the saints through pictorial representations. Dedicated to a life of poverty, possessing no individual property, and looking to a future life for their reward, they devoted every thought and faculty to the one pious purpose, and out of this grew the exquisite art of illumination, the perfection of Gothic architecture, the craft of painting on panel and on wall, and the glories of stained glass. Even when the art of painting ceased to be carried on by the monks and became the object of the professional artist, the skill in preparing certain pigments still remained in the monastery, and the artist engaged himself in painting sacred pictures and preserved towards his craft the religious feeling by which the monks had been inspired.

There is no blasphemy, therefore, no thought of irreverence, in directing the measurement of time while a pot of colour is boiling by the repetition of paternosters. The decoration of the Church was itself an act of prayer, and all that appertained to it, such as the preparation of a pigment, was therefore an act of devotion. When, therefore, we come to examine the MS. of the monk Theophilus, of the twelfth century, an unknown inhabitant of some German monastery, we find this spirit pervades the whole, and is beautifully expressed in the prefaces by which each book dealing with some artistic craft is introduced. Of these the preface to the third book, dealing with the working of metals, is the most beautiful, and is worthy of quotation as one of the most perfect revelations of the thought and feeling of a monk engaged in artistic crafts in a mediæval monastery.

Nothing is known of Theophilus, but it is probable from internal evidence that he travelled far and wide, even as far as Constantinople, to collect his receipts, and his elaborate defence of the duty of decorating the House of God is perhaps an answer to the iconoclasts and the persecution of the artists in the eighth and ninth centuries, begun under Leo the Isaurian. His work is divided into three books, the first of which deals with painting, the second with glass-manufacture, and the third with work in the metals, and the title of the MS. is *Diversarum Artium Schedula*, by Theophilus, called also Rugerus.

Before considering briefly the book dealing with painting, I shall quote in full the whole of the beautiful preface to the third book as a revelation of the attitude towards art and religion of a monk of the Middle Ages. For the following translation of it I am myself responsible, as the rendering given by Hendrie does not quite satisfy me. I have read with pleasure the translation by Mr Coulton in his *Mediæval Garner*, of which I have made full use.

Preface to the Third Book of *Diversarum Artium Schedula* by Theophilus.

David, of special excellence among the prophets, whom God foreknew and predestined before time was, and whom, because of his simple and humble mind, he chose as one after his own heart, and made a prince over his own people, and strengthened him with his holy spirit that he might rule with the nobility and prudence worthy of so great a name; with all his mind intent on love of his Maker, spoke these among many other words, 'Domine dilexi decorem domus tuæ'. And it is lawful for a man of such authority and such breadth of understanding to speak of the habitation of the celestial host in which God rules with inestimable brightness over the hymns of the celestial choirs as a house; towards which indeed his very bowels yearned saying: 'Unam petii a Domino, hanc requiram, ut inhabitem in domo Domini omnibus diebus vitæ meæ'; or as the sanctuary of a faithful breast and purest heart in which verily God dwelt; a refuge for which the same glowing desire again breathes forth in prayer, 'Spiritum rectum innova in visceribus meis, Domine'. Nevertheless, it is certain that he longed to make beautiful the earthly House of God, the place of prayer. For he made over to Solomon his son almost all the treasures in gold and silver, in brass and in iron, of the House, of which he himself had desired with the most ardent passion to be the author, a privilege denied to him because of the frequent spilling of human though hostile blood. For he had read in Exodus that God had given to Moses the command to build the tabernacle, and had chosen by name the masters of the work, and had made them full of the spirit of wisdom, understanding and knowledge for the designing and making of things in gold and silver, in brass and precious stones and wood, and in every kind of craftsmanship; and through devout meditation he knew that God was graciously pleased with such furnishings, which he designed to be put together under the guidance and influence of his Holy Spirit; and he believed that nothing of this kind could possibly be brought to pass without the divine impulse.

Therefore, beloved Son, do not hesitate, but with abundant faith believe that the Spirit of God has filled thy heart, since thou hast furnished the House in so comely a manner and with so many diverse works of art; and lest perchance thou shouldst be distrustful, I will clearly and reasonably prove that whatsoever of craftsmanship thou art able to learn, to comprehend, or to invent is gifted to thee by the favour of the seven-fold spirit.

Through the spirit of wisdom thou knowest that all created things proceed from God, and without him nothing is; through the spirit of understanding thou art become capable of invention, in whatsoever order, variety, or measure thou wouldst exercise it on various works of art; through the spirit of counsel thou hidest not the talent gifted to thee by God, but with all humility labourest openly, and teachest loyally, showing everything to those desirous of learning; through the spirit of ghostly strength thou dost shake off all slothful lethargy and completest with abundant force whatever thou hast diligently begun without delay; through the spirit of

15

knowledge with which thou hast been endowed thou controllest thy invention from an abundant heart, and that which flows out in perfect form from the well stored mind thou boldly usest for the good of all; through the spirit of true godliness thou dost direct the time, the manner, and the quantity of thy work; and lest the vice of avarice and greed should creep in, thou dost fix the price of thy labours by a pious consideration of the virtues of moderation; through the spirit of the holy fear thou dost reflect that thou art able to do nothing from thyself, and that thou canst neither possess nor will anything except through the gift of God; but, believing, trusting, giving thanks, thou ascribest to divine compassion what thou knowest, what thou art, and what art able to be.

Having drawn near, O dearest Son, to the House of God with a confidence inspired by these covenants with the virtues, thou hast adorned with so much grace both walls and ceilings with different works and with different colours, setting forth the semblance of the paradise of God blooming with all kinds of flowers, green with grass and leaves, cherishing the souls of the saints with crowns of varied worth. Thou hast in a measure disclosed to the beholders everything created praising God its maker, and hast caused them to proclaim him wonderful in all his works. Nor can the eye of man decide upon which work first to fix his glance; if he beholds the ceilings, they bloom like tapestries; if he regards the walls, they have a splendour of paradise; if he looks up to the wealth of light from the windows, he admires the marvellous beauty of the glass and the variety of that glorious work. And if perchance a faithful soul beholds an image of our Lord's Passion revealed in drawing, he is pierced with compassion; if he beholds what torments the saints have endured in their own bodies and what rewards reaped in the life of eternity, he lays hold on the lesson to observe a better life; if he beholds the joy of heaven and the torments of the flames of hell, he is inspired with hope through his own good deeds and is shaken with terror by reflecting on his sins.

Act therefore now, virtuous man, happy before God and men in this life, happier in the future life, through whose labour and zeal so many sacrifices are offered up before God; henceforth be kindled by a more splendid genius, and begin with the full exertion of thy mind those things which are still wanting among the utensils of the House of the Lord. These are the chalices, candelabra, incense-burners, vials, pitchers, caskets of sacred relics, crosses, missals, and other things which are required as needful and expedient for the ceremonies of the Church.

If thou wouldst fashion these, thou must begin in the following order.

16

T H E   O B J E C T of this book is to sum up for the student of the history of art what we know about pigments, mediums, and methods of painting from Egyptian times to the present day.

In order to compare the æsthetic value of the painter's art at different periods, we have not only to study the æsthetic aim and skill of hand of the painter, but also the limitations imposed on him by the material in which he worked.

The study of the materials used is, therefore, an essential part of the training of the student of the history of art. In fact, I would go further, and say that part of his training should be to practise for himself the use of the various media employed at different times. The only school I know which has adopted this practice is the Department of Art in Harvard University.

The plan I have adopted in this book is to divide my subject into two periods.

First: The Classical Period, dealing with painting in Egypt, Greece, and Rome, and ending with Pliny.

Second: The Mediæval Period, from the rise of Christian Art to 1550, the date when Vasari's *Lives of the Painters* was published.

Vasari, after describing the priming of a panel or a canvas, tells us that the pigments are ground in linseed or walnut oil, which is their medium, and then applied to the primed canvas. That is, he describes the modern method of painting in oil.

On studying the mediæval period, the reader is bewildered by the mass of the material contained in a large number of manuscripts with recipes for pigments, mediums and varnishes.

I have come to the conclusion that while useful information is to be obtained from these manuscripts, they require very critical examination.

I have found one authority who is absolutely reliable, writing clearly and simply from his own experience as a painter, namely, Cennino Cennini. He was born in Padua about the middle of the fourteenth century. Though himself of humble origin, he has a supreme artistic pedigree. He was the pupil for twelve years of Agnolo, the son of Taddeo Gaddi, who learnt his art from Giotto, and he has the unusual gift for a craftsman of writing clearly and specifically about his own craft.

His treatise is also a fascinating revelation of the man himself and of the

B

world he lived in of pious artists devoted to the service of the church. I quote on page twelve the dedication of his book, which reveals his equal reverence both for the saints and for the masters who taught him.

I propose, therefore, to quote very largely from him, as I cannot improve on his own description of methods and materials. He has left for us a detailed description of the practice of the fourteenth century, in which century the illumination of manuscripts, painting in egg, and in stand oil, and Buon Fresco, were brought to perfection, followed by the burst of genius, using all these methods, in the fifteenth century.

In the third period dealing with the later centuries, the subject of most interest is the development of brushwork as a method of conveying the æsthetic aim of the artist, which is best studied by means of photomicrographs of the work of the great painters.

Finally, I have something to say about varnishes, and have a concluding chapter dealing with the methods of detecting forgeries and other fraudulent practices, and a chapter dealing with Persian illuminated manuscripts.

May I make some suggestions as to further reading? Daniel V. Thompson, after laborious burrowing into the manuscripts on painting buried in the Vatican library, has summed up what we know about the literary side of the subject in his book *The Materials of Mediæval Painting*. His chapters on the use of gold both as a decorative material and as a pigment are especially interesting. I believe I was the first to point out the use of gold as a yellow pigment in a picture by Holbein.

He has also published the most accurate text and the most accurate translation of Cennino Cennini's book on the art of painting by collating the three known MSS., and written a book on the practice of tempera painting and on the technique of manuscript illumination.

Lady Herringham, who was an accomplished painter in tempera, has also published a translation of Cennino Cennini, with a most interesting introduction and conclusion.

The Scientific staff in the Art Department at Harvard University, Mr R. J. Gettins and Mr G. T. Stout, have written an Encyclopædia dealing with mediæval art. An excellent translation with commentaries has been made of Vasari's introduction to his *Lives of the Painters*, dealing with technique, by Louisa S. Maclehose. There are innumerable papers in *Technical Studies*, the publication of the Harvard Art Department, and the Tempera Society has also published some interesting papers, one especially on fresco painting.

Among earlier writers there is Eastlake's book, *Materials for a History of Oil Painting*, Mrs Merrifield's translation of Mediæval MSS., and the learned labours of Professor Berger and many others.

These older authorities form interesting reading, but ultimately it is for the chemist and not for the antiquarian to decide what pigments, media, and methods were used.

The three most important MSS. in the history of painting are the Lucca MS. (eighth century), which contains the last mention of the use of wax as a medium and the first mention of varnishes made by dissolving resins in linseed oil. The second is the *Schedula* of Theophilus Presbyter written in the twelfth century, and containing a full account of methods of painting, the manufacture of glass both for stained glass windows and mosaic, and work in silver and gold. The student who wishes to make a full acquaintance with various copies of this MS. is referred to a paper published by Professor Thompson in *Speculum*, vol. VII, April 1932. The third MS. is the *Book of the Art* by Cennino Cennini written in the fifteenth century from which I quote largely in the following pages.

Throughout this book I have used the phrase "Buon Fresco" to mean painting on wet lime with pigments mixed with water. When I write of a tempera medium, I mean a medium in which the binding material is mixed with or dissolved in water, such as gum, size, and white and yolk of egg.

I wish to thank the following who have given me assistance in the production of this book :

Mr I. E. S. Edwards, Egyptian Department, British Museum; Messrs Pearson Bros. for information about the properties and manufacture of Stand Oil; Messrs Winsor and Newton, Roberson, and Reeves for supplying me with samples of pigments now out of use, and Messrs Winsor and Newton for the information they gave me about sign writing and the illustration of the brushes used, and Mr Philip Hill of Bond Street for valuable information about the varnishes used on old violins.

The following have given me permission to quote from their publications and to reproduce illustrations : His Grace the Duke of Westminster ; Messrs George Allen & Unwin; Messrs Macmillan; Messrs Seeley Service;

Mr Peter Davies ; the Oxford University Press ; the Society for the Promotion of Christian Knowledge ; and *Technical Studies*, published by the Fine Art Department, Harvard University.

The following have given me permission to reproduce photographs from their collections : The Directors of the National Gallery, London, the National Gallery of Scotland ; the Antwerp Museum ; the Department of MSS., British Museum ; and Dr Delporte of Brussels.

D. V. Thompson's writings on Mediæval Painting have been of the greatest value, and I am specially indebted to Professor Forbes of Harvard University for writing the Preface.

I am indebted to Mr McConnachie of A. H. Baird, Edinburgh, for the photomicrographs reproduced in the book, and to Messrs Faber and Faber for permission to reproduce the illustrations in colour from their *The Virgin and Child*.

THE TECHNIQUE OF THE GREAT PAINTERS

B*

CHAPTER I

Painting in Egypt, Greece, and Rome

APART from the Egyptian Blue which I shall describe presently, and the dull green glass produced when the blue was overheated, the Egyptians had few pigments before the time of the Ptolemies, when Roman pigments were introduced. They had a red and a yellow ochre, used whitening for white, and prepared a charcoal black. They also had malachite, which was doubtless found in their copper mines, and they used gold for decorative purposes. For media they had the gum of the acacia, which grows freely in Egypt today, and they also had size and may have used egg as a medium. One recipe exists for a mixture of egg and gum arabic. Gold leaf on the Death Masks was cemented on with white of egg. White of egg was the favourite cement for gold leaf in the middle ages, and is even used today.

Owing to the fact that the objects found are often afterwards treated with varnish, it has been difficult to decide whether they used any varnish themselves. Thanks to Professor Baldwin Brown, I was able to secure three fragments of coffin lids which had not been treated in any way. On one, the pigment was quite easily removed with a wet finger, and on analysis the medium proved to be gum arabic.

In the case of another fragment, the surface of the wood had been roughened, so as to leave little fibres of wood sticking up over the surface. On this had been laid a layer of sand mixed with size, and on the top of this a white gesso on which painting was done. On the third fragment, of the nineteenth dynasty, the whole had been covered with a reddish coloured varnish, which was readily soluble in alcohol. I was not able to determine what resin had been used. Probably the resin had been collected while still in a semi-liquid condition and then, perhaps, slightly warmed and laid on as a varnish, as we have no reason to believe that the Egyptians knew anything of drying oils, or had any means of obtaining a volatile medium in which they could dissolve a resin. Apparently the use of this varnish was confined to the nineteenth and twentieth dynasties.

EGYPTIAN BLUE

The Egyptians made a remarkable discovery, only to be equalled by those of the chemists of today. They found out how to make a most beautiful blue which was used for thousands of years by the countries in the Mediterranean basin. The earliest example I have examined belongs to the eleventh dynasty. We find it on the frescoes of Knossos, long before the Greek civilisation we know, and it was still in use throughout the Roman Empire up to the second or third century, when it disappears, and is never seen again.

The furnaces in which Egyptian blue was made, containing cakes of blue, are found buried under the sand in Egypt, suggesting that some catastrophe had taken place, and the skilled artificers, who had preserved the secret for thousands of years, had been killed by some invading army.

The Egyptians had not found out how to glaze earthenware, but in the earliest period they were accustomed to carve beads and small ornaments out of a soft sandstone. They found that by covering these beads with a paste containing copper ore and desert alkali, and putting them in a furnace, they obtained the beautiful blue glaze we are familiar with.

It must have occurred to some ingenious maker of beads that if he crushed the sandstone to a powder and mixed all the ingredients together and heated them, he might get a blue pigment with which he could paint. Ultimately, he succeeded in doing so.

The secret of how the blue was made has not been easy to discover, in spite of the fact that Vitruvius has given us a recipe in his book on Architecture, in which he says that the blue was made by heating in a furnace a mixture of desert alkali, copper ore, and sand. Several chemists have attempted more or less successfully to reproduce this blue; Sir Humphrey Davy, Fouqué, and Russell have all worked at it, but not succeeded in establishing definitely the conditions of manufacture. On reading through their researches, it seemed to me that what was required was to repeat Fouqué's experiments under the conditions not available to him, of keeping the mixture at a constant measured temperature for several hours in a crucible furnace heated by an electric current. Dr Miles and Mr McLintock agreed to assist me in these experiments, and I kept the little electric furnace beside my desk, so that it should be under constant observation.

Having made a mixture of copper oxide, fusion mixture, calcium carbonate, and pure white sand, in the proportions given by Fouqué, I heated it for some hours in the electric furnace at 800° C. On examining the frit, there were some indications that the sand had been slightly attacked, a little blue having been formed. I then raised the temperature to 900° C. for several hours. The copper oxide was dissolved, but instead of obtaining the blue, a green glass had been formed. On now lowering the temperature to 830° C. and keeping it constant for several hours, beautiful blue crystals were slowly separated from the green glass. The correct temperature for forming the blue was, therefore, proved to be between 830° C. and 850° C. and by grinding and reheating the frit between these temperatures, it was possible to convert the whole of the copper oxide into Egyptian Blue. I had the pleasure of sending Flinders Petrie a small brick of blue, and some years later Sir Robert Mond made some of the blue according to my recipe, to repair an Eygptian vase in his collection—no modern blue had the right tint.

To keep a furnace for several days within such a small range of temperature would be no easy matter today with all our modern measuring apparatus. It is, therefore, very remarkable that the Egyptians were able to do this successfully.

Professor Berger states that in the case of the paintings on temples which are partly flooded by the Nile, the paint has not come off. If that is so, they must have been treated with wax after the manner practised in Rome.

The Egyptians learnt the art of dyeing at an early date, and fabrics have been found which have been dyed with madder. The discovery of a madder pigment, therefore, is of interest. It seems to have been prepared by boiling together madder, lime and gypsum, and was of a dull red colour. I found it quite possible to prepare a dull red pigment by this method. With this exception the Egyptians do not seem to have used any organic pigments. The preparation of paper was as follows: it was prepared from the pith of the papyrus reed, which used to grow freely in Lower Egypt but is now extinct. The pith was cut in thin slices and the slices laid side by side and beaten with a mallet on a slightly sloping slab so as to drain off the sap. They were then brushed over with flour paste and a fresh lot of strips laid on at right angles. In this way the papyrus was made, several strips being laid over and over and hammered together.

The wax portraits of the second century discovered by Flinders Petrie at Hawara I will discuss later.

The two main literary sources for obtaining knowledge about the pigments used in classical times are Pliny and the seventh book of Vitruvius on Architecture, with some additional information from Theophrastus. In addition to these literary sources, we have the actual analysis of Egyptian pigments and pots of paint found at Pompeii and elsewhere, and of the pigments found on Pompeian and other Greek and Roman frescoes. To deal with all this mass of information in detail, and to quote the results of the various chemists and give every reference to the texts of Pliny and others, would be tedious in the extreme. The larger number of pigments have been identified without doubt, and the fringe of obscure references left is not of enough importance to delay us. We shall find a most excellent and complete palette available for the Greek or Roman painter in the time of the Empire.

Before, therefore, going into the question of media, I shall proceed to describe briefly the actual pigments that were in use. We find, as might be expected, that the earth colours were well known. It may be necessary here to explain in passing that the earth colours, as they are roughly called, consist of clays, which owe their peculiar tint to the presence of compounds of iron and, in some cases, of manganese. The rich yellow ochres are entirely stained by compounds of iron, while the siennas contain some manganese, and the umbers almost entirely owe their colour to the presence of this mineral. The red ochres also owe their colour to the presence of iron, and are, in many cases, native, such as red haematite, or they can be obtained by roasting the yellow ochres. In addition, there is a green pigment known as terre verte which owes its colour to iron, and which was largely used in ancient times. It is no longer possible to get such fine varieties of this pigment as were once obtainable. These pigments merely require mining, grinding, and floating over, and have always formed and will always form an important part of the artist's palette, both for beauty and for durability. In addition to these, there are other native pigments, which, however, require more careful preparation. Many of the ores of copper are beautiful blues and greens, and of these the finest is azurite, a blue carbonate of copper. Good specimens of azurite merely require to be ground to give a beautiful pigment, which is very suitable for painting in many media. It is, however, somewhat sandy in character, and does not lend itself well to painting in oil. Other ground copper ores, such as malachite, yield fine greens which are somewhat sandy in character. There are in addition, cinnabar, the red sulphide of mercury, which is, in fine specimens, very nearly as brilliant as the artificial preparation known as vermilion; and among yellows there is none more beautiful than orpiment, the native sulphide of arsenic. There are also other tints of this sulphide of arsenic which seem to have been used for pigments. Then among the whites we have a large number of white earths, of which chalk is, of course, the most important. This may be said to exhaust fairly completely the pigments which can be found native, and which do not require artificial preparation. In modern days, orpiment has disappeared from the artist's palette, cinnabar has been replaced by the artificial preparation known as vermilion, and the copper blues have ceased to be used. It is evident from Pliny's account that all these pigments were well known in classical times, and the next point of interest is how far artificial pigments were known and manufactured. There are certain descriptions in Pliny which are obscure and difficult to follow, and therefore it is not possible to identify all the pigments used in classical times; but at any rate a large number of them can be clearly distinguished. White lead, for instance, was prepared very much in the way in which the best English white lead is prepared today, by the corroding action of the vapour of vinegar and the carbonic acid gas of the air upon lead plates, the white corrosion formed on the surface of the lead being collected and washed and used as a pigment. It seems also from Pliny's account that white lead was used as a face powder, so that it is evident that its deadly qualities were not then understood. In the preparation of lead from its ores the discovery of the various oxides of lead had evidently been made in Pliny's time, as he describes more than one of these, and among them evidently red lead, which has also been identified on Roman frescoes. There is some confusion obvious in his account between red lead and vermilion, the word *minimum* being applied by him to the vermilion; but the existence of the pigments is without question. The preparation of verdigris by the action of vinegar on copper was also known, and the beautiful Egyptian Blue has already been referred to. Pliny's accounts of this blue are very vague, but it is clearly described by Vitruvius.

In addition to these mineral pigments, the use of dyes for the preparation

27

of pigments was evidently well understood, and many of the common vegetable dyes were obviously in use, such as weld, woad, and madder. They seem to have been accustomed to stain chalk or gypsum with these dyes, and so to prepare pigments. The description of such a madder dye from Egypt has already been given, and also the fact that the chemist John has discovered the use of a vegetable yellow lake in Egypt. Pliny speaks of dyeing some of the mineral pigments with a view to enhancing their colour. It is possible that this may have been done, but is not very probable. In addition to these dyes, there are two others which require to be mentioned. One of these is the famous *murex*, the shellfish from which the imperial purple dye was obtained. Vitruvius speaks of thickening this with honey, and Pliny speaks of its being precipitated by means of a white earth which was used for the cleaning of silver, and which was probably infusorial earth, as this earth has the property not only of absorbing certain liquids, and therefore forming the basis of dynamite, but also of absorbing and fixing certain aniline dyes, and it may well be that it also had the property of taking up the *murex* purple. Pliny speaks of it as having a greater attraction for the purple than wool. The use of dyes, of course, involved the knowledge of mordants, and Pliny describes at great length a substance of the name of *alumen*, which, we know as Rock Alum today. The next dye which requires to be referred to is *kermes*. This dye is due to an insect of the same kind as the cochineal insect which lives on the prickly oak round the shores of the Mediterranean, and forms dry, hollow, red berries in appearance. This was used both for dyeing and the preparation of pigments in classical and mediæval times, and it is not until the introduction of the cochineal from Mexico after its conquest by Cortes, that *kermes* begins to be replaced by the more brilliant cochineal. Its use has been revived in recent times for dyeing tapestry by the late William Morris. Blacks were prepared either from lamp black by burning resins and fats and collecting the smoke, or from charcoal, or apparently from bones. Pliny tells us that painters have been known to go so far as to dig up half-charred bones from the sepulchres for the purpose of making black. Pliny also mentions the preparation of black from dried vine leaves and from grape husks, both of which are known to give a black of fine quality at the present day. In addition to these substances, there is a reference in Pliny which is quite unmistakable to the use of indigo, which, he tells us, can be obtained either from the scum of the dyer's vats, which would mean the dyers who were using woad, or from India, and he describes its properties with such exactness that there can be no question but that indigo is the substance referred to. We must, therefore, suppose that, at any rate in the first century A.D., indigo was exported to Rome from India. In conclusion, there is another reference to a resin which is used for colouring varnishes, and which was known as dragon's blood, and which also comes from the East. This reference is of so quaint a character that it is worth quoting. In the eighth book of his *Natural History*, Pliny describes the antipathy between the elephant and the dragon, stating that they are perpetually at war, and that the contest is equally fatal to both, as the dragon envelops the elephant in its coils, and the elephant, vanquished, falls and by its weight crushes the dragon. The whole details of this conquest are given at some length.

GREEK PAINTING

If we are to accept the verdict of Pliny, who is our principal authority, the Greek painters were as famous in the early years of the Roman Empire as the Greek sculptors.

He complains of the inferior work of Roman painters, while the millionaires of the day paid huge prices in the auction room for pictures painted by Greek Old Masters.

None of the Greek paintings has survived. All we have are the Pompeian frescoes, which are probably reproductions by inferior artists of the work of the great painters of Greece, and from Hawara, in Egypt, funeral portraits in wax, of about the second century A.D., some of which have considerable merit. If we ask ourselves what media for painting the Greeks had, doubtless they had size, fish glue, and also probably gum arabic and other gums. In addition they had, of course, egg as a painting medium, both yolk and white. They do not seem to have known the property possessed by the drying oils of being converted into elastic films when exposed in thin layers to the air.

The extraction of olive oil is, of course, very old, and walnut oil, which is a drying oil and has been used in painting, can be separated from the walnut merely by boiling with water, but the extraction of linseed oil from the seed is much more difficult. Pliny mentions linseed poultices, but never linseed oil, the drying oil universally used today.

The fact that they varnished their ships with beeswax and painted with beeswax as a medium, is an additional argument in favour of the conclusion that they did not know the properties of the drying oils as paint mediums.

They were also probably ignorant of spirits of turpentine and of rectified petroleum. The crude petroleum was used as a lighting oil in Babylon, but the discovery of the art of distillation comes much later.

Pliny mentions heating wood tar and closing the mouth of the vessel with a fleece and wringing out the fleece from time to time, but the discovery of the art of distillation is accredited to one, Cleopatra, of the third century A.D., the first of the Lady Doctors.

Knowledge of the art of distillation was probably confined to the alchemists, as it is not till the fifteenth century that Aqua Vita became an article of commerce, and it is not till the sixteenth century that we get recipes for varnishes made by dissolving resins in rectified petroleum or spirits of turpentine.

I have gone into this somewhat fully, as owing to a careless translation of Pliny, it has been assumed that the Greek painters used an emulsion of beeswax in turpentine or a wax soap, as a medium for painting.

Before considering in detail the method of painting in wax, let us read what Pliny has to say about painting.

In the thirty-fourth chapter of the thirty-fifth book, he proceeds to tell us of the more famous painters with the "brush", but makes no mention of their medium.

He mentions first Apollodorus of Athens, and then Zeuxis of Heraclea. *"Through the gates of Art thrown open"* (by Apollodorus) *"Zeuxis of Heraclea passed in the fourth year of the ninety-fifth Olympiad and brought the brush—for it is still of the brush we are speaking—to the great glory at which it was already aiming."*

Passing on to Chapter Thirty-nine, he goes on to tell us about famous painters in wax.

Turning to the contents table, we find the different schools of painting clearly defined :—

"Qui pencillo pinxerint.
De avium cantu compescendo.
Qui encausto cauterio vel cestro vel pencillo pinxerint."
"Those who painted with the brush.
On silencing the singing of birds.
Those who painted in encaustic with the cauterium, the cestrum and the
brush."

Let us first consider the two methods of painting in wax, one with the cauterium and the other with the brush. For the first method, sticks of wax mixed with pigments were prepared. A hot bronze tool called the cauterium was used to melt and mould the coloured wax in low relief. Excellent examples of this method have been found at Hawara.

The painting with the brush is a little more difficult to understand. Little pots containing beeswax and pigments were placed on a hot plate, the two stirred together and the brush dipped in. If we try this, we shall find that the wax will be found to set before it can be transferred to the picture.

Now Pliny in describing painting with the brush writes, *"Ceris pingere ac picturam inurere quis primus excogitaverit, non constat"*, and this has been assumed to mean that the picture was *first* painted and *then* fixed by heat.

The significance of the use of *ac* for *and*, was not appreciated. There are two words for *and* in Latin; when one event follows after another *et* is used, when they both happen simultaneously *ac* is used.

Owing to careless translation, it has been assumed that the beeswax was emulsified with spirits of turpentine to paint the picture and heated afterwards to fix the paint in position.

Recollecting that Greece has so much warmer a climate than we have here, I tried warming the panel, and then got a young artist to paint me a picture of a daffodil. Each stroke of the brush was quickly laid on and left. The result cannot be distinguished from an oil painting.

I found that a well-known member of the Scottish Academy had painted a wax picture, placing his canvas before a hot fire, which looked just like an oil painting. Professor Petrie confirmed my conclusion and said that he had found indications in the Hawara portraits that the sun had been too hot and the wax had run.

31

Pigments mixed with wax were used to decorate ships. It was, in fact, the universal painting medium.

The expert employed by the Soviet to clean the Greek Ikons told me they have found wax paintings up to the sixth century. After that tempera is used.

The last mention of wax as a medium occurs in the Lucca MS. in the cathedral at Lucca, supposed to be of the eighth century.

The funeral portraits found at Hawara are all we have of what must have been a successful technique in Greece. Pliny does not tell us what medium was used by painters with the "brush".

Plate 1

PLATE I GRECO-ROMAN PORTRAIT

National Gallery No. 1265

These Greco-Roman portraits, ranging from about A.D. *40 to* A.D. *250, were found in the cases of mummies discovered in a cemetery at Hawara in the Fayum, Egypt, by Professor Petrie in 1888.*

These portraits, painted in wax, illustrate the use both of the cauterium and the brush. The face is modelled by the cauterium and the accessories laid in with the brush.

34

CHAPTER II

Buon Fresco in Classical Times

THE METHOD of painting on walls which is called Buon Fresco consists of painting pigments mixed with water on damp plaster. Lime is slightly soluble in water, and consequently the wet lime is dissolved and, as the plaster surface dries, is deposited in a colloidal state round the particles of pigment, cementing them to the wall. It is then slowly changed by the action of carbonic acid gas in the air into the insoluble carbonate of lime. This method of painting was used in painting the frescoes in the palace of Knossos, and in the painting of frescoes in Pompeii, and also used in the Middle Ages and by the Italian fifteenth- and sixteenth-century painters. We shall have to consider in some detail this method of painting on walls, as under suitable conditions of climate and pure air it has proved remarkably permanent and, in addition, by its very limitations has resulted in a very high standard of design and of drawing. It was considered, for instance, by Michael Angelo, as the highest expression of the painter's craft. The day may come when artists will revive this method of decorations in climates like that of California, when once we arrive at a method of heating which does not involve loading the air with sulphur acids.

Before going on to discuss in detail the methods employed for painting on wet lime, there is a variation of this method of wall painting which is worthy of notice. The Egyptians had plentiful deposits of gypsum, and found that by heating gypsum they could produce a cement. Gypsum consists of sulphate of lime combined with a certain amount of water. On heating to a low temperature for a short time, some of this combined water is given off. The gypsum, having been ground to powder, is heated in shallow circular iron pans with constant stirring, so as to make "plaster of paris". On mixing this powder with water, the water rapidly combines with it, forming needle-shaped crystals which are all matted together, and this is the process of the setting of the plaster. If the gypsum is heated to a higher temperature, it loses more water and we get a product which sets very slowly but ultimately becomes very hard. In Nottinghamshire the floors of old houses are made of reeds mixed with this slow-setting cement. It was prepared by piling up lumps of gypsum and coal and setting them on fire. Doubtless the cement from gypsum which was used in building the Great Pyramid was prepared in this way.

If they used this product to plaster a wall, it is possible to paint pictures on it according to the method used in Buon Fresco. Gypsum, like lime, is slightly soluble in water, and consequently, if pigments mixed with water are painted on a damp surface of gypsum cement, they will be attached to the surface as the cement dries, just as in Buon Fresco.

I understand that the oldest wall paintings in Egypt have been painted on a gypsum plaster without any binding medium. When I was asked by Lucas about this, I tried some experiments and found it quite possible to paint frescoes in this way. I understand that a similar process had been used in some of the prehistoric frescoes in India.

To return to Buon Fresco on lime, Mr Noel Heaton has made an exhaustive enquiry into the painting of frescoes in the palace of Knossos. He finds they were painted on a very thick plaster of reeds and lime and that there is no binding medium; so they are examples of genuine fresco.

The walls of Pompeii are covered with frescoes, and the question as to how they were painted has given rise to considerable controversy. Of course, it is obvious that the Greeks and Romans possessed several alternative methods. They had both gum and glue and egg, all media capable of being used in painting on a dry wall, and it is obvious from the account given by Vitruvius, an architect living in the time of Augustus, that they also understood the art of painting on wet plaster. The following is a translation of his account.

"When the cornices are finished, the walls are to be trowelled as roughly as possible, and thereafter, when the trowelling is somewhat dry, over it the directions of the sand-mortar are to be so traced out, that in length it must be true by the rule, in height by the plumb-line, and the angles by the square. For thus the surface of the plaster will be faultless for pictures. When this (first coat) is slightly dry, a second is to be laid on, and then a third. The firmer and sounder the laying on of the sand-mortar, the more solid and durable will the plaster work be. When, besides the trowelling, not less than three coats of sand have been set out, applications of marble-dust are to be used. This stuff is to be so tempered that in spreading it does not stick to the trowel,

but the iron comes out of the mortar clean. A coat of marble-dust having been laid on and getting dry, another rather thin coat is to be applied. When this has been beaten and well rubbed, another still finer is to be put on. Thus with three coats of sand and as many of marble, the walls are so firm that they cannot crack or become defective in any way. And, moreover, solidity being secured by rubbing with planes, and smoothness from the hardness and sheen of the marble, the walls will give out with great brilliance colours applied with polishings. For colours, when they are carefully laid on damp *plaster, do not get loose, but are for ever permanent: for this reason, that the lime, losing all its moisture in the kiln, is so dry and porous that it readily imbibes whatever chances to touch it, and solidification taking place from the mixtures of the various potentialities whose elements or first principles are brought together, the resulting substance, of whatever it is composed, when it becomes dry, is such that it seems to have special qualities peculiar to itself. Thus plaster work which is well executed neither becomes rough from age nor when it is washed does it give up the colours, unless they have been laid on carelessly and on a dry surface. If, therefore, plasterwork on walls is carried out as above described, it will be firm, lustrous, and very durable. But when only one coat of sand and one of marble-dust are used, its thinness renders it liable to be easily broken, nor can it take on a proper brilliance from the polishings, owing to its lack of substance. For just as a silver mirror when made from a thin plate gives back a wavering and uncertain image, but if made from a plate of solid temper takes on a high polish and reflects to the spectators bright and faultless images, so plastering, when its substance is thin, is not only full of cracks, but also quickly decays, while that which is firmly compacted of sand-mortar and marble, when it has been rubbed with many polishings, is not only glistening, but also clearly reflects to the spectators the images falling on it. Greek plasterers, indeed, use not only the above methods to make their work firm, but also putting the lime and sand together in a mortar, they have it thoroughly pounded with wooden staves by a number of men, and use it after it is so prepared. Hence from their old walls, people cut out slabs and use them as panels, and those plaster slabs so cut out for panels and mirrors have fillets in relief round them."*

We shall have to consider this translation very carefully, but before doing so it is necessary to point out an error in the accepted Latin text. When considering technical processes it is necessary to be quite sure that the accepted text is correct, as the probability is that the scholar who is responsible for the accepted text knows nothing of the technical process he is describing. Unfortunately, English texts of the Classics cannot be trusted, as when the scholar responsible for the text makes an alteration which is not justified by the original manuscript there is no indication that he has done so. In the case of German additions, any such alterations are shown by printing at the foot of the page the wording of the original manuscript. I found it, therefore, necessary to get German editions both of Pliny and Vitruvius.

In my translation of Vitruvius you will find "for colours when they are carefully laid on *damp* plaster do not get loose but are for ever permanent".

Turning to the Latin text we find that the word used is *udo—wet*, which would finally decide the nature of the method employed in painting fresco. But on turning to the German text, we find a note as to the actual manuscripts from which the English text was prepared and that in all four of these manuscripts the word is *nudo—bare*, and not *udo*.

The manuscripts referred to are as follows: Harleian MS. Brit. Mus. 2767 (about ninth century). Scletstatensis, 1153 (tenth century). Wolfenbuttelensis Gudianus, 69 (eleventh century). Epitomati Vitruvii, Wolfenb. Gudian., 132 (tenth century). These four are regarded by Rose as the most reliable authority for the original text.

It is obvious that the use of the "bare" leaves it an open question whether the plaster was dry or wet.

To return to Vitruvius. If we take the whole of the paragraph in which the word *udo* occurs, I think it is obvious that he is referring to damp plaster. He tells us that *"the colours are permanent because solidification takes place from mixtures of the various potentialities whose elements or first principles are brought together, the resulting substance, of whatever it is composed, when it becomes dry, is such that it seems to have special qualities peculiar to itself"*. It is obvious that Vitruvius realised that some change had taken place by which the wet plaster, on drying, had bound the pigments. In fact, if he had known of the action of carbonic acid gas on the lime, the change of a word or two would have converted this sentence into a correct description of the chemical changes which had taken place. It is, therefore, probable that the original word was *udo* and that the transcribers of these manuscripts have made a mistake.

The main objection made to the use of Buon Fresco in Pompeii is that evidently large panels on which the pictures were painted, were prepared at one time, and it is suggested that they would dry too quickly for painting in Buon Fresco to be carried out. It seemed to me, therefore, worth while to make some experiments on a mortar prepared according to directions given by Vitruvius. This mortar is about five inches thick, so that it holds moisture for some time.

It will be noted that Vitruvius requires treatment of the plaster by beating, rubbing with planes, and polishing. Professor Berger assumes that such polishings would require an introduction of a soap of some kind, on the lines of the Italian method of making imitations of marble.

I was therefore determined to find whether these polishings were not possible if I employed a skilled plasterer. I had some shallow boxes made and filled them with mortar according to the directions given by Vitruvius, and when the coats of marble-dust and lime had been laid on, the plasterer came over them each day with the edge of his trowel, the plaster remaining wet for days, and he gradually brought up a polished surface just like polished marble. Owing to the thickness of the plaster and the closing of the pores by polishing, I found that I had got plenty of time to paint on colour mixed with water, and this colour became bound by the dissolved lime, adhering excellently well. I believe that it is now agreed that the coloured panels on which the painting was done were prepared as Vitruvius tells us. The final painting is, I understand, slightly raised from this surface, and I obtained my best results by gently pressing on the painted surface with a suitable tool, while the plaster was still damp. I gather that the chemical evidence is a little inconclusive as to whether an organic medium was used in the final painting. A medium may have been used if the polished panel had been allowed to get dry, or on another occasion, the painting done on a wet plaster, but I think it very doubtful if these frescoes would have remained so firmly adhering if they had depended on any organic medium.

The experiments I have made on beeswax potash emulsions have proved very unsatisfactory, and with all due respect I feel the late Professor Berger has built up with great ingenuity an entirely unnecessary series of assumptions about the Pompeian frescoes.

Apparently the statues and interiors of the Greek temples were painted by laying a thin coat of plaster on them, the pigments being laid on this plaster mixed with some medium which was probably size. After they were dry, Pliny tells us, they were "polished with candles", a process known as *ganosis*. I find if, after the painting with size is dry, I rub it over very gently with a lump of beeswax, a thin layer of beeswax is left, which can then be polished with a soft handkerchief, thus forming a protective coating and giving the shiny surface which it is evident the Greeks preferred to a dead surface.

CHAPTER III

Buon Fresco

THEOPHILUS, writing in the twelfth century, gives us an account of wall painting in which he advises that a dry plastered wall be wetted and a little lime mixed with the paint. This cannot be regarded as a satisfactory method, as under such circumstances the union to the plaster would not be nearly so complete as when the pigment is laid on the fresh wet plaster. The next reference is to the manuscript carried away by Monsieur Didron from the monastery at Mount Athos. This manuscript is supposed to be of the fifteenth century but claims to be the teaching of a painter of the eleventh century. Didron found the monks painting on walls exactly according to the directions given in this manuscript, which is known as the *Hermeneia*. Two layers of lime plaster were laid on the walls about half a centimetre thick. The first layer consisted of lime and chopped straw, and the second layer was mixed with tow or flax. Evidently the practice followed was similar to that used in the Palace of Knossos, where there was no addition of sand or marble-dust. The drawings were then laid out and the painting began straight away, simple washes of colour being laid on. The somewhat mechanical method by which the shading and tints of flesh and drapery were built up corresponds closely to the instructions found in the manuscript of Theophilus, and was doubtless of Byzantine origin.

An interesting fact is that no medium but water was used, that the painting did not begin until the plaster had been drying for three days, and it took some five days to complete, so that during this time the fixing of the pigments depended on the dissolving out of fresh lime from the surface of the plaster, which would already have been considered too dry for painting on according to the practice of the fifteenth century in Italy. There seems to be no reason why fresh lime should not be dissolved out of the lime mortar for some days after it has been laid on. The only precaution mentioned in the *Hermeneia* is that the painting is begun before a crust has formed on the surface of the lime.

Mr Traquair, who has had the opportunity of examining many Byzantine frescoes in the East, tells me that he has found in many cases a fresh fresco painted over the old one, a thin coat of fresh mortar about one-eighth of an inch thick having been laid over the surface before a new picture is painted.

It is interesting to note that the polishing of the ground is advised in the *Hermeneia* receipt, thus connecting the mediæval method of painting fresco directly with the classical method as described by Vitruvius. Evidently, where the painting of the surface was delayed, the polishing and closing in of the plaster was regarded as essential.

I shall now come to the account of fresco painting given by Cennino Cennini, which represents fourteenth-century practice in Italy. I shall discuss the history of the Cennino Cennini manuscript on fourteenth-century painting more fully in a subsequent chapter. I have come to the conclusion that amid the vast masses of material on pigments, mediums, and methods of painting, which are to be found in manuscripts and books on painting, dating from the eighth to the eighteenth century, and including Vasari, we have one absolutely reliable writer, Cennino Cennini, and I quote on occasion fully from his text, using for that purpose the translation by Lady Herringham—a text which should be compared by students with the Italian text published by Professor Thompson as the result of collating the three original manuscripts we possess. I shall, therefore, begin by quoting the account Cennino Cennini gives us of Buon Fresco as practised in his time in Italy.

Chapter 67. The manner of painting on walls, that is, in fresco, and of colouring or painting the flesh of the faces of young persons.

In the name of the Most Holy Trinity, I will now put you to colouring. I begin first with painting on walls, and shall teach you step by step the manner in which you ought to proceed. When you are going to paint on walls, which is the most delightful and charming kind of work that there can be, procure, in the first place, lime and sand, both of them well sifted. If the lime is very rich and fresh, it will require two parts of sand, the third of lime. Grind them well together with water, and grind enough to last you fifteen or twenty days. Let it rest for some days till it be quite slaked; for if any heat remains in it, it cracks the plaster (intonaco). When you are going to plaster, first sweep the wall, and wet it well—you cannot wet it too much; and take the well-stirred lime, a trowelful at a time, and spread it over once or twice, till the intonaco becomes quite even on the wall. Afterwards, when you are going to work, remember to make the surface of the mortar quite rough (bene arricciato) with a good tooth (rasposo). Then, according to the subject of figures you have to make, if the intonaco is dry, take some charcoal, and design and compose, and take every measurement carefully, first striking on one line, taking the centre of the space, and another for the horizon. The perpendicular line by means of which the horizontal one is obtained must be made with a plumb-line. Then put one foot of the large compasses on the top of this line. Turn the compasses half round on the underside; then put the leg of the compasses on the point of intersection of these two lines and make the other half circle above, and you will always find a cross on your right hand by the lines intersecting each other. Do the same on the left hand which will give you two crosses, and the line between will be exactly level. Then draw with charcoal, as I have before directed you, historical pieces and figures, and arrange your spaces always equal. Next take a small and pointed bristle brush, with a little ochre without tempera, as liquid as water, and continue to draw your figures, shading them as you did with water-colours when I taught you to draw. Afterwards take a bunch of feathers and thoroughly brush away the charcoal.

Then take a little sinopia without tempera, and with a finely pointed brush mark out the nose, eyes, hair, and all the extremities and outlines of the figures, and let these figures be correctly set out in every measurement which helps you to realise and project the figures which you have to paint. Then make your fringes (or ornaments, fregi) and accessories as you please. Take some of the above-mentioned lime, stir it well with a trowel till it is like the consistence of ointment. Then consider how much you can paint in a day; for whatever you cover with the plaster you must finish the same day. Sometimes in winter, in damp weather, working on a stone wall, the plaster remains fresh till the next day; but if you can help it do not delay, because when painting in fresco, that which is finished in one day is the firmest and best, and is the most beautiful work. Then spread over a coat of thin intonaco, and not too much, first wetting the old intonaco. Next take your large hog's hair brush in your hand, steep it in clean water, beat it and wet your plaster with it, and then with a slip of wood as wide as the palm of your hand, rub round and round over the wetted intonaco so as to remove the lime where you have put too much, and put more where there is not enough, and thus make your plaster quite smooth. Then wet the plaster with the same brush if necessary, and with the point of the trowel, which must be very clean and smooth, rub all over the intonaco. Then place your plumb-line as usual, and measure as you did on the underlying intonaco. Let us suppose that you can paint in one day

43

the head only of a young male or female saint, such as that of our most Holy Lady. Having thus smoothed the lime of your intonaco, procure a glazed vessel; the vessels should be all glazed and shaped like drinking or beer glasses, with a good heavy bottom that they may stand firmly, and not spill the colours. Take as much as a bean of dark ochre (for there are two kinds of ochre, light and dark); and if you have no dark ochre, take light ochre ground very fine; put it into your vase, and take a little black the size of a lentil, mix it with the ochre; take a little bianco sangiovanni (lime-white) as much as the third of a bean, and as much light cinabrese as will lie on the point of a penknife; mix all these colours thoroughly together, and make them flowing and liquid with water, without tempera. Make a sharp brush of fine soft bristles, which may be introduced into the quill of a goose, and with this brush indicate with proper expression the face you are going to paint (remembering that the face is divided into three parts, namely, the forehead, the nose, and the chin, with the mouth), and with your brush nearly dry, put on this colour, little by little, which is called in Florence verdaccio, and in Siena bazzeo. When you have sketched out the form of the face, if the proportions or any other thing should displease you, with a large brush steeped in water, by rubbing over the intonaco, you can efface and repair what you have done. Then take a little verda-terra, very liquid, in another vase, and with a hog's-bristle brush, without a point, squeezed with the fingers and thumb of the left hand, begin to shade under the chin, and all those parts of the face which should be darkest—under the lips, the corners of the mouth, under the nose, and under the eyebrows, making the shade darker near the nose, a little on the edge of the eye towards the ear; and in the same manner making out with judgment (sentimento) the whole face and hands, which are hereafter to be coloured with flesh colour. Next take a pointed minever brush and strengthen all the outlines of the nose, eyes, lips, and ears, with the verdaccio. There are some masters who now, when the face is advanced thus far, take a little bianco sangiovanni tempered with water, and seek out the high lights and reliefs in proper order; then give the rosy colours to the lips and cheeks; then wash over the whole with the flesh colours very liquid with water, and the colouring is done. It is a good plan to retouch afterwards the high lights with a little white. Some wash over the whole face with the flesh colour first; they go picking out with a little verdaccio and flesh colour, retouching with a little flesh colour, and the work is finished. This plan is adopted by those only who know but little of the art; but do you follow the method of colouring which I shall point out to you, because Giotto the great master followed it. He had Taddeo Gaddi the Florentine for his

44

disciple for four and twenty years, who was his godson. Taddeo had Agnolo his son;
Agnolo had me for twelve years, whereby I gained this manner of colouring; which
Agnolo coloured with more charm and freshness than Taddeo his father.

First take a small vase; put into it (a tiny morsel is enough) a little bianco sangio-
vanni, and a little light cinabrese, about as much of one as of the other. Temper them
very liquid with clean water; then with a soft bristle brush, squeezed between the
finger and thumb as before, go over the face when you have finished putting it in with
verda-terra; and with this red colour (rosetta) touch in the lips and the roses of the
cheeks. My master was accustomed to put the colour in the cheeks nearer the ear than
the nose, because it assisted in giving relief to the face, and then he softened the
rosiness well into the surrounding colours. Then have three small vases, and make
three shades of flesh colour, so that the darkest may be darker by one half than the
rosetta, and the other two each lighter than the other in regular gradations. Now take
the little vase containing the lightest tint, and with a very soft bristle brush without
a point take some of this flesh colour, squeezing the brush with the fingers, and pick
out the reliefs of the face; then take the vase containing the middle tint of the flesh
colour, and paint a naked figure. Afterwards take the third vase of flesh colour, and go
to the edges of the shadows, but always taking care at the contours that the verda-
terra should not lose its value, and in this manner keep on softening one flesh tint
into another, until it is all covered as well as the nature of the work will permit. But
mind that if you would have your work appear very brilliant, be careful to keep each
tint of colour in its place, except that with skill you soften one delicately into the
other. But seeing others work and practising with your hand, will make you perceive
better than seeing it merely written. When you have painted in these carnations, make
from them a tint much lighter—indeed almost white, and use this above the eyebrows,
on the relief of the nose, the tip of the chin, and the upper eyelids; then take a sharp
pointed pencil of minever, and with pure white put in the whites of the eyes, and above
the tip of the nose and a little on the fulness of the mouth (della proda della bocca),
and so touch tenderly such lights. Then put a little black into another vase, and with
a brush mark out the outlines of the eyes, the contour of the nose, the brows and the
mouth, and shade a little under the upper lip, which must be a little darker than the
under. Before you finish these outlines thus, take the said brush and with verdaccio
retouch the hair; then with the said brush, put on the lights of the hair with white,
and with a watery wash of light ochre, and a soft bristle brush, cover over the hair as
you did the carnations. Mark out the extremities of the shadows with dark ochre, then

with a small and very pointed pencil of minever put on the lights of the hair with bianco sangiovanni and light ochre. Retouch the outlines and extremities of the hair with sinopia as you did on the face, all over. And this is sufficient for you for a youthful face.

Chapter 72. The manner of colouring walls in secco, and the proper temperas.

Any of the colours used in painting fresco may also be used in secco; but in fresco, some colours cannot be used, as orpiment, cinnabar, azzuro della magna, minio, biacca, verderame, and lacca. Those which may be used in fresco are giallorino, bianco sangiovanni, black, ochre, cinabrese, sinopia, verdeterra, and amatisto. Colours used in fresco must be made lighter with bianco sangiovanni, and if you wish the greens to preserve their green tint, make them lighter with giallorino; when you would have them take the colour of sage, add bianco. Those colours which cannot be used in fresco must be made lighter by the addition of biacca, giallorino, and some-times orpiment, but orpiment is very rarely used; indeed I think it is superfluous. To make a light blue, take three of the same kind of small vases as I directed you to use when speaking of the carnation tints and cinabrese, and prepare them in the same manner, except that where you then used bianco, you should now use biacca, and temper them all. Two sorts of tempera are good, but one is better than the other. The first tempera consists of the white and yolk of an egg, into which are put some cuttings of young shoots of a fig tree; beat them well together; than add some of this tempera moderately, neither too much nor too little, to each of the vases, like mixing half wine with half water; then work with your colours, either white or green or red, as I directed you in fresco-painting; and you will proceed with your draperies in the same manner as you did in fresco, with a careful hand, waiting, however till it (the plaster) is dry. If you use too much tempera, suddenly the colour will crack and peel off the wall. Be wise and skilful. Remember before you begin to work, if you wish to make a drapery of lake, or of any other colour, take a clean sponge, and having mixed the white and yolk of an egg with about two porringers full of clean water, and mixed them well together, with the sponge squeezed half dry pass this tempera over the whole of the space on which you have to paint in secco, and ornament in gold, and then colour freely as you please. The second kind of tempera is the yolk of the egg only; and you must know that this tempera is of universal application on walls, on panels, and on iron, and you cannot use too much of it, but be wise, and take a middle course.

46

Before we proceed further, I would have you paint a drapery in secco in the same manner as you did in fresco, with cinabrese. Now I will have you make one of ultramarine blue. Take the three vases as usual; into the first put two parts azure and the third biacca; into the third, two parts biacca and one part azure; mix them and temper them as I have directed you. Then take the empty vase, that is to say, the second; put into it an equal quantity from each of the others, and stir all well together with a hog's bristle brush, or, if you like, a minever brush blunt and firm; and with the first colour, that is to say, the darkest, go round the outlines, marking out the darkest folds. Then take the middle colour and lay the flat tint of these dark folds, and mark out the light folds of the light side of the figure. Then take the third colour, and lay the flat tint of the light folds which come on the lighted side, and unite them with each other, softening and laying in the flat tints as I showed you how to do in fresco. Take the lightest colour, add to it some biacca with tempera, and put on the high lights of the folds of the light part. Then take a little pure biacca, and retouch a few of the highest lights as the nude shape of the figure requires. Afterwards with pure ultramarine pick out the darkest folds and outlines, in this way retouching (leccando, lit. licking) the drapery according to its situation and colours without soiling or mixing them one with another except to soften them. And in this manner use lake and all other colours with which you work in secco.

It will be noted that Cennino Cennini had no blue which could be used on the wet plaster and therefore the blue was laid on the dry plaster mixed with egg.

CHAPTER IV

The Mediæval Pigments

BEFORE proceeding to identify the pigments used in mediæval times as determined by chemical and optical analysis of the pigments actually used to paint illuminated manuscripts and pictures, it is necessary to say something about the large number of manuscripts which we possess containing recipes for the making of pigments and media. The most important of these manuscripts were translated by Mrs Merrifield, and others have been translated since by Professor Berger and others. I have spent many weary days testing out these recipes in the laboratory.

It is, I think, obvious that these manuscripts were compiled, probably principally in the monasteries, by men who were neither painters nor colour makers, but collected recipes, copying from age to age without discrimination and often writing down impossible formulæ.

Fortunately for the sanity of the student of art, Professor Thompson has, after investigating many manuscripts in the Vatican Library which had never been examined before, collected all the *documentary* information available from these sources, into his book *The Materials of Mediæval Painting*, published by Allen and Unwin.

On examining these records, we find that along with recipes with which we are already familiar, such as the separation of ultramarine from lapis lazuli and the preparation of lakes, there are a large number of recipes for the extraction of colours from plants. The coloured juice was squeezed out, strips of linen were dipped in alum, and then in the juice, dried and dipped again and again, until there was a thick layer of pigment which could be used as we use water-colour paints.

Now such pigments are notoriously fugitive, and are not to be found on the illuminated manuscripts, which, with the exception of a lake, Tyrian purple and a yellow used on the Books of Hours of the Flemish painters, were painted with permanent mineral pigments. How can this discrepancy be explained? There can be no doubt that these pigments were prepared by the monks and used by them.

It is true that Professor Thompson has pointed out that pigments could be used for book illustration which could not be used for the painting of pictures exposed continuously to daylight. To take an example, we are all familiar with crimson lake made from cochineal, but would not regard it as sufficiently permanent for the painting of pictures, but we have a curious piece of evidence that it would be sufficiently permanent for illustrating books. I have prepared the lakes from sapanwood, which are so frequently referred to in these manuscripts, and found them to be a little more fugitive than crimson lake. Now there is a manuscript on pigments, known as the Venetian manuscript of about the fifteenth century, which has capital letters painted in red, and the red has not faded. In the manuscript itself we are told that these initial letters were painted with a lake made from sapanwood, so that we have here sufficient evidence that lakes of about the permanence of crimson lake could be used for book illustrations.

But the vegetable juices are much more fugitive than crimson lake and, therefore, we still have to decide for what purpose they were used.

On searching for an explanation, I found one in Cennino Cennini, to whom we can always refer with confidence, as he was a skilled craftsman who himself has published a very selected palette of permanent pigments for the painting of pictures, a list which agrees closely with the one I have obtained from the examination of actual illuminated manuscripts.

In the beginning of his *Book of the Art*, Cennino Cennini gives some instructions for the training of the young artist. He tells the beginner to practise laying on smooth tints of colour on sheets of paper, and then to begin drawing figures and colouring them. In Chapter 10, after having explained how to shade in black and white, he goes on to say "In the same manner you may shade with colours and clothlet tints (*Pezzuole*) such as miniature painters use". It is evident, then, that he was quite familiar with these pigments prepared from the colours of plants and regarded them as quite suitable for tinting exercises, but he never refers to them again and uses quite a different list of pigments when he comes to the painting of pictures.

Let us now suppose that we are about to paint some miniatures on vellum in a book which is to form a permanent addition to the monastic library. We should first require to make preliminary drawings and colour them, making many alterations, until we had arrived at a satisfactory scheme of colour and design. Having done that on paper, we would use that as our guide in painting the miniature on vellum. In painting a picture on the vellum, we would use permanent pigments, but these pigments were difficult to obtain and expensive to buy; therefore, for the preliminary study, we would use these pigments from plants which the monks could prepare for themselves from the plants to be found within the neighbourhood of the monastery, or very likely, grown for the purpose in the monastic garden. This is a simple explanation of why these manuscripts are full of recipes for making these fugitive pigments, while the actual pigments used for the final painting were nearly always mineral pigments of a permanent character. Some of these permanent pigments, the monks would, no doubt, prepare in the monastic laboratory, such as the ultramarine extracted from lapis lazuli. Cennino Cennini tells us that vermilion was made by the monks by the heating of sulphur and mercury, and could be obtained from them. Other pigments would be purchased, coming from many and distant sources.

The study of the manuscripts led to no conclusion as to what pigments were used by the mediæval painter. I had tried many of their recipes and found some of them workable and studied the properties of the products. In other cases the recipes were not workable and sometimes obviously absurd. "Take a lusty he-goat and feed him on ivy leaves" etc. . . . .

In these recipes no distinction was made between permanent pigments and pigments of the most fugitive character prepared from the coloured juices of plants. In Cennino Cennini alone, do we find a selection of pigments chosen for their permanent qualities.

I felt that this was not sufficient, and that it was necessary to determine the pigments actually used by identifying samples on dated documents.

I selected illuminated manuscripts for the following reasons. Their date is usually known, they have not been in the hands of the restorer or the improver, and the pigments are much more easily identified under the microscope than pigments buried in oil or covered with varnish.

I was fortunate enough to have the opportunity of examining several illuminated manuscripts from which I could take very minute particles for identification by microchemical analysis. With these as a guide, I was able to train myself to identify pigments through the microscope and with the help of the Lovibond tinted glasses.

The information obtained from illustrated manuscripts produced in the monasteries or by the Flemish painters of the fifteenth and sixteenth centuries, was confirmed by an examination of the *Coram Rege* rolls in the Record Office, which have a portrait of the King on his Throne painted in colours on the title page from 1500 to 1700, and also by examining Venetian Ducali and many pictures.

The main results obtained were, that the pigments on European manuscripts were Ultramarine or Azurite, Malachite, or a transparent green, of which I shall say more, or a basic insoluble verdigris used in the fifteenth and sixteenth centuries, red lead and vermilion, orpiment, a lake and gold.

The pigments used on the Byzantine and Scoto-Irish manuscripts were different. Up to the end of about the ninth century, the Byzantine pigments were used throughout Europe, consisting of a dull badly washed ultramarine, a flaky orpiment, vermilion or red lead, and the Tyrian purple in place of a lake. This list of pigments continued unaltered in the Byzantine and Scoto-Irish manuscripts up to the thirteenth century. On European manuscripts the Tyrian purple was replaced by a lake, and the ultramarine continually improved until it reaches perfection in the twelfth century.

We shall now proceed to discuss in detail the various pigments used in painting illuminated manuscripts, beginning with Byzantine. The earliest Byzantine manuscript is in the British Museum. It is a page of the Gospel, of the sixth or seventh century. We find on this manuscript a green, which is apparently malachite, a badly washed ultramarine, and a magnificent purple which I take to be the Tyrian purple prepared from the Murex shellfish. The next Byzantine manuscript is painted with vermilion, orpiment, malachite, badly washed ultramarine and a Tyrian purple. This is the complete Byzantine palette, which is repeated over and over again well into the thirteenth century. Later manuscripts after 1300 show a marked deterioration, containing only vermilion, badly washed ultramarine, and a lake instead of the Tyrian purple.

This Byzantine palette was universal through Europe up to about 900, and then became differentiated. Except on the Scoto-Irish manuscripts, which I shall shortly begin to discuss, I have never found the Tyrian purple on European manuscripts except on one about 900 A.D. A large number of the Byzantine manuscripts were dyed purple with the Tyrian dye, with silver and gold lettering. We now come to what are known as Scoto-Irish manuscripts. The first conversion of these islands to Christianity took place in Ireland. From Ireland, missionaries were sent to the Island of Iona, who proceeded to convert the Scottish people to Christianity, their mission being associated with the name of St Columba. From Iona, missionaries were sent into Northumberland under St Aidan, who established his headquarters on Holy Island off the Northumberland coast, where he founded the monastery known as Lindisfarne. St Augustine was sent by the Pope on a special mission to England and founded monasteries in the south, such as Winchester, London and Canterbury, and entered into unsuccessful negotiations with the Welsh Christians, but does not seem to have come in contact with the Celtic missionary movement in the north. There were certain differences of a minor character between the monks of St Augustine, who followed the strict Roman practice, and the Celtic monks, who differed on several minor points, such as the correct date for Easter.

The final settlement between the monks in Northumberland and the Roman rule, was made by Saint Wilfrid in the seventh century, and we do not find again the use of the Byzantine palette south of the Tweed. On the other hand, what are known as Scoto-Irish manuscripts painted in Irish and Scottish monasteries, are painted with the Byzantine pigments up to the thirteenth century. The use of these pigments disappeared in Scotland after Queen Margaret introduced the Roman rule into the Scottish monasteries, and disappeared in Ireland after it was invaded by Henry II, who was ordered by Pope Adrian IV to bring the Irish monasteries under the Roman rule.

We find on the Scoto-Irish manuscripts a Tyrian purple of their own manufacture made from the *Purpura Capillus* which is found off the Irish Coast. They used red lead instead of vermilion, probably prepared by roasting white lead, malachite for a green, a flaky orpiment, the source of which I have not been able to discover, and a badly washed Byzantine ultramarine.

As we have already seen, the preparation of ultramarine from lapis lazuli continually improved throughout the centuries, reaching perfection in the twelth century, but this in no way influenced the practice of the Scoto-Irish School.

The two most magnificent examples of Celtic illumination are the Lindisfarne Gospel and the Book of Kells. It is claimed that the Lindisfarne

Gospel was painted in Lindisfarne before 800 A.D. and was buried in the tomb of St Cuthbert in Durham Cathedral, from which it was removed at the time of the Reformation. We find on it, red lead, orpiment, malachite, badly washed ultramarine, and the native Tyrian purple which is not quite so scarlet as the Mediterranean variety. In addition, on the Lindisfarne Gospel, a yellow ochre has been used and there is a pink wash over some of the pages, which is probably made by the use of the Tyrian purple. The illuminations in the Book of Kells are very similar and the pigments are the same. We do not know where the Scoto-Irish manuscripts were painted, whether in Scotland or in Ireland. The decoration with colour is very simple, but the same Byzantine pigments are repeated again and again, while on the English manuscripts we find a lake used instead of Tyrian purple and, as I have said, a continued improvement in the ultramarine. It is difficult to know from what source the Irish pigments came. I have never found the flaky orpiment anywhere else than on these manuscripts. The Tyrian purple they no doubt prepared themselves, and if they were able to get lapis lazuli, may have prepared an ultramarine by the old Byzantine recipe, but the existence of this palette for so long suggests a direct communication with Europe which was not over the Dover Straits. Malachite is found in Ireland.

The Celts were widely distributed throughout Europe and they made two invasions of our island, taking permanent possession and either destroying or absorbing the Iberians. They were workers both in bronze and iron and had reached a considerable standard of civilisation, but they were principally remarkable for introducing a new conception of decoration, based upon the arrangement of lines and patterns, followed by the introduction of circles, curves and spirals, and abstract representation of plants, animals and human beings. Many magnificent examples of Celtic work have been found in the barrows in which they buried their warriors, on the crosses which they erected to the dead and in the illumination of manuscripts within their monasteries. The most perfect examples we possess are the initial letters in the Lindisfarne Gospel, illuminated by a monk in Lindisfarne before 800, and in the Book of Kells in Ireland, the product of Irish and Scottish monasteries.

Ultramarine—The examination of English and European illuminated manuscripts made it possible to follow the history of ultramarine prepared from lapis lazuli. On the early manuscripts we find a dark dull blue which, on examination through the microscope, is evidently contaminated by a large quantity of the mineral which lapis lazuli contains. In the case of Byzantine and Scoto-Irish manuscripts this blue never improved, but in the case of English and European manuscripts we find a gradual improvement which finally culminates in a perfect ultramarine in the psalter of Queen Melissenda of Jerusalem, painted between 1131 and 1144. This manuscript had been painted partly by Eastern Monks and partly by Western Monks, the Eastern part as well as containing the perfect ultramarine, contains a fine specimen of Tyrian purple. This, as I have said, is the first appearance of a perfect ultramarine. It next appears on Italian manuscripts, and then on English manuscripts about 1200, so that the recipe seems to have come from the East and gradually crossed Europe. The first appearance of a recipe for the correct method of preparing ultramarine is in the manuscripts by Alcherius of the thirteenth century. It is an interesting application of the method of separating minerals by difference in surface tension which is made so much use of in the separation of ores today. The finely ground lapis lazuli is worked up into a paste with wax, resin and oil, and is kept with frequent kneading for some days. It is then placed under warm water containing a little potash lye and kneaded under the water; the blue separates leaving the other minerals behind. I shall quote later the recipe as given by Cennino Cennini. The remarkable fact is that while this manuscript was probably being painted in Jerusalem, the Byzantine monks continued to use their old dull ultramarine. Wherever the recipe came from, it was not from Persia, as we do not find a fine ultramarine on Persian manuscripts until the fifteenth century. I imagine it must have been the discovery of some Arabian chemist, although it took so long to penetrate into Persia.

Azurite—the native blue copper carbonate, appears and disappears as a blue replacing ultramarine on illuminated manuscripts. I think probably that what we may commonly call the house-painter's blue was an inferior azurite used throughout the centuries, but occasionally crystalline deposits were found in copper mines, which were so perfect and beautiful in colour, that they replaced ultramarine. I find, for instance, an azurite occurring on some illuminated manuscripts from 1250 to nearly 1400, then it appears again towards the end of the fifteenth century, and finally disappears from the artist's paintbox about 1650, being replaced by an artificial copper compound, blue bice.

I have already said something about the history of lakes. Occasionally, I have seen on a manuscript a faded pigment that might have been a yellow and occasionally I have come across a beautiful mauve colour, but we take it that illuminated manuscripts were painted with the pigments I have mentioned.

A very interesting use of gold occurs on some of the English manuscripts of the tenth and eleventh centuries, and more especially in King Edgar's Charter to Winchester, the letters in which are painted in gold. This gold, on examination under the microscope, was seen to consist of little rounded particles, and I matched it exactly with some river gold obtained from a stream in Scotland. During this short period, some English manuscripts were painted with this gold instead of the ordinary gold paint made by pounding gold leaf, mixed with a little tallow in mortar.

Verdigris was prepared by the slow corrosion of copper plates plunged among grape skins; the acid in the fermenting grape skins attacking the copper, which becomes covered with a green crust, which is scraped off and is the pigment known as verdigris. Chemically it consists of a mixture of basic acetates of copper. It was regarded with great suspicion by Cennino Cennini, who advises glue as a medium and tells us it must not be mixed with white lead. Judging by the examination of old pictures in which it has been used, it has sometimes stood the test of time and in other cases has turned black. There are two possible explanations of this turning black. In the first place I have found that it is slightly soluble in linseed oil, and that it slowly diffuses through the dry film. If it comes in contact, owing to this diffusion, with a sulphide such as cadmium yellow, the result is that the two pigments act on each other and turn black. This may be the reason why Cennino Cennini advises painting it on with size instead of oil. I cannot confirm his statement that it acts on white lead. Another reason for its turning black is that it is easily acted upon by an alkali, and therefore may have been blackened by using an alkali soap to clean a picture. It is easy, therefore, to understand why its behaviour in pictures has been so variable, and why careful painters like Cennino Cennini regard it with suspicion. In the old recipes we are told to purify it by the addition of vinegar. This, by converting it into a soluble acetate, would make it more dangerous to use.

I have found that if it is boiled with a small quantity of water I get a separation of a green which is quite insoluble in water and, therefore, can be much more safely used as a pigment. It exactly matches the crystalline green used on the Flemish Books of Hours, which has remained quite unchanged. Probably, therefore, they prepared the variety of verdigris they used in this way. I have found one very interesting instance of its use. The skies in Watteau's pictures are painted with a very beautiful blue. This blue is a mixture of real ultramarine with a little verdigris.

I made a curious discovery on a German manuscript, supposed to be about 1100 A.D. We are already familiar with verdigris and malachite as greens, and we also know that, according to the recipes contained in the manuscripts dealing with painting, sap green and the green from iris were known. This German manuscript had a green which was very brilliant, quite transparent, with no crystalline structure, and giving the reactions for copper. I was able to imitate it exactly by dissolving verdigris in turpentine, Canada balsam and the liquid resin from the cedar. In the case of the Canada balsam and the liquid resin from the cedar, the product was insoluble in water, alcohol, and chloroform. In one of the samples I examined, there was a small particle of azurite, which suggested that it had not been made from the verdigris obtained by the corrosion of copper plate, but that the azurite had been dissolved in vinegar evaporated to dryness and then dissolved in a liquid resin. The first recipe for this copper resinate occurs in the De Mayern manuscript, but it was probably known far earlier than this, as I have repeatedly found in illuminated manuscripts a transparent non-crystalline green which matches this pigment, and which I have ventured to describe as copper green. The latest example of it was found in a manuscript of about 1540, but it is overlapped by the use of verdigris from about 1400.

Before going further into this matter, it is necessary to mention a property possessed by these oleo-resins. In 1907 I published in the transactions of the Society of Arts a research undertaken to test the statement made by Eastlake in his *Materials for a History of Oil Painting*, that an oil varnish protects a fugitive pigment from fading.

It is unnecessary to describe here in detail the various experiments I made, and it is sufficient to give the conclusions arrived at.

Oil and oil varnishes do not protect fugitive pigments, but pure resins such as mastic dissolved in turpentine do protect, and of these resinous media the best protection is obtained by using the oleo-resins of the larch, silver fir and cedar. I suggested at the time that these oleo-resins might have been used by the early oil painters to protect fugitive pigments.

To return to the copper resinate found in the German manuscript: I found repeatedly in illuminated manuscripts up to the fifteenth century, a transparent green which showed no crystalline structure, and was, therefore, neither malachite nor verdigris. The only other transparent green I know is the chlorophyll green obtained from vegetable sources by the monks. It is a much duller green than the green in the German manuscript, and is notoriously fugitive. When we come to examine the Flemish Books of Hours of the fifteenth century, this green is replaced by a verdigris green, the preparation of which I have already described, but a beautiful green is found on the pictures by Van Eyck and his followers, which has remained brilliant through the centuries. I had no opportunity of examining through the microscope the green on the dress of the woman in the Arnolfini portrait, but I examined a fifteenth century German picture in the Edinburgh National Gallery, in which the same beautiful green appears. When examined under the microscope, this green showed no crystalline structure, but was remarkably transparent with here and there minute particles floating in it which have not been completely dissolved. This green is not seen at later dates, and when we come to the Dutch Little Masters, we know from Hoogstraten that they used a blue mixed with a yellow lake which has evidently faded.

Beyond the fact that this green does exist on this German manuscript the rest is an assumption on my part. On the other hand, it seems to me inconceivable that so beautiful a green, which could be obtained simply by warming up verdigris with a little Venice turpentine, was not known throughout the Middle Ages.

Lakes—The painter today is familiar with madder lakes and crimson lake, and he may also have heard of a lake made from Persian berries, which is yellow and called Dutch pink. But he no longer uses the lakes known to the painters of the Middle Ages. The making of a lake is a simple matter, and was known in the time of Pliny. A vegetable colouring matter, to take an example, is boiled with potash lye, is filtered, and alum added. Alum mixed with the potash lye alone, as long as the lye is not in excess, gives a white flocculent precipitate which when dried and ground in oil gives a colourless transparent medium. When the alum is added to the solution of the dye the alumina attracts the dye to itself, and instead of the white flocculent precipitate we get a coloured precipitate, which on washing and drying can be used as a pigment, and is what the artists call a "lake". The process may be reversed, that is the dye may be boiled with the alum and the potash added after. In this way a very large range of pigments can be made from colours extracted from vegetable and animal sources. The whole process is closely allied to dyeing and alum has long been used by dyers from early times for the fixing of dyes upon material. Most of these lakes are very fugitive. The only permanent lakes we know are the madder lakes. The mediæval lakes were obtained from several sources. A dyewood from Ceylon known as *verzino*, *brixillium*, or sapanwood, and a dye obtained from different varieties of the cochineal insect known as *Grana* or *Kermes*. According to Professor Thompson, several varieties of this cochineal insect were sold under the name of *Kermes*; but the main source of supply in Europe was the *Coccus Ilicis*, which grows on the leaves of the prickly oak. The prickly oak is found in Spain and Portugal and other countries round the Mediterranean. The insect looks like a little red bead. It was reintroduced for dyeing by William Morris, and I have frequently prepared a lake from his supply. It has about the same permanency if exposed to light as crimson lake made from Mexican cochineal.

Another dye introduced somewhere in the twelfth century was stick lac from India, where another of these insects attacks the tree, on which it grows, forming a resin known as shellac. I have also prepared an excellent lake from stick lac and it is rather more permanent than crimson lake owing probably to its containing some of the resin. The stick lac is boiled in water in India to separate the shellac and the dye from each other. The evaporated solution of the dye is sold as a pigment and is very likely, from the description given by Cennino Cennini, to be the lake to which he refers. The lake from sapanwood is even more fugitive than crimson lake.

All these lakes have a purplish colour and are not so bright as crimson lake, but produce a magnificent crimson when painted over vermilion.

On examining the lakes used on illuminated manuscripts, I found that many of them had faded, but that in the case of a large number of manuscripts from 1150 to 1500, a lake was used which had not faded, and was matched by the lake I had myself prepared from stick lac. I have therefore in my table of pigments entered this durable lake, which is so often used, as "lac lake" because it matches the lake which I prepared, but I have no knowledge of its composition.

None of these lakes which we have discussed is of the same order of permanency as the madder lake which the artist uses today. The question therefore arises as to when madder lakes were first introduced. There are very few references to madder in the recipes given in the manuscripts, but the absence of these recipes may be due to the difficulty of making fine madder lakes from the madder root. The madder root contains the dyeing principle alizarine, but the dye is not in a free state and the root has to be subjected either to a process of fermentation or to treatment with slightly diluted sulphuric acid to set free the dye. The process, after fermentation, of producing a bright dye known as Turkey red, is very elaborate and difficult owing to the madder root's containing other dyeing and resinous principles. We find consequently that the madder dyers in the Middle Ages formed a separate Guild with special privileges.

The recipe mentioned by Professor Thompson, boiling together a dyewood with madder root, would not dissolve the alizarine but would stain the lake with brown resinous substances from the madder root.

The making of madder lakes is also a difficult process. The old artist colour firms such as Winsor and Newton, Reeves, and Le Franc, possess recipes which are not to be found in any text book, the published recipes being quite useless.

The synthetic production of the dyestuff alizarine has of course facilitated the production of lakes, but they have not replaced the delicate tints of the true madder lakes made from the root. The most brilliant madder lake I know is produced by Le Franc, and it took me a long time before I succeeded in producing a lake to match theirs. I am not surprised therefore that no recipes are to be found in the *Secreti* for the making of a madder lake, and it does not follow that the Guild of dyers in madder did not make and sell madder lake as a side-line.

In the accounts relating to St Stephen's chapel, decorated in the time of Edward III, occurs a mention of a pigment called sinople which cost thirty shillings a pound, and in the manuscript of Alcherius we read that sinople is a colour redder than vermilion, and is made from madder. As the word sinople or *sinopia* is used both by Pliny and Cennino Cennini for red ochre, we are here faced by the unreliability of mediæval names for pigments.

There is a manuscript in the Advocates' Library in Edinburgh known as the *Speculum Vitæ Christi*, which was painted between 1465 and 1489. I have obtained from this manuscript particles of a lake which proved on analysis to be madder lake. The existence of a madder lake at this period has been confirmed in the laboratory at Harvard University Art Department. We can state definitely that madder lakes were used from this period. It does not follow that they were not used earlier, as I have not had the opportunity of obtaining a sample of a lake from earlier manuscripts.

On the whole, the evidence is that while lakes were produced before 1500 which were sufficiently permanent for book illustration, they were not permanent on pictures.

Having prepared these lakes from the old recipes, and glazed them over vermilion, I compared them with the crimson robes in Italian fifteenth and sixteenth century pictures. In all cases the lakes had faded, the robes looking a brownish red against my samples. When I see a brilliant lake on an old master I suspect that the picture restorer has been busy.

The following diagram summarises the results of my investigations into the mediæval pigments. I have already discussed the possibility of a green made by dissolving verdigris in Venice or Strasbourg turpentine. Wherever I found a bright transparent green, with no crystalline structure, on a manuscript, I have entered it on this diagram as copper green, and wherever I found a permanent lake which was matched by the lac lake I had myself prepared, I have entered it as lac lake.

Any student who wishes to study the details of the pigments used on illuminated manuscripts, will find them in my book *The Pigments and Mediums of the Old Masters*.

FIGURE 1 : Graph showing dates of use of various pigments

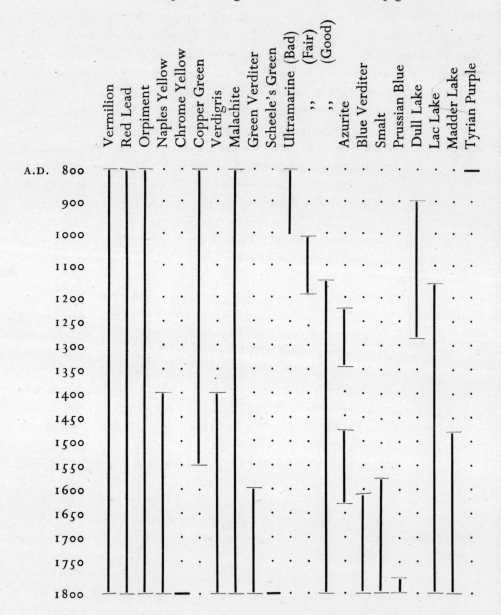

NOTE: The date of the pigments used in Byzantine and Irish monasteries is not included in the table.

CHAPTER V

The Pigments described by Cennino Cennini

HAVING described the pigments found on illuminated manuscripts, let us compare them with the list given by Cennino Cennini. They are as follows:

Red. Sinopia (red ochre), cinabrese (red ochre and white), cinnabar, minium, amatisto (Haematite), dragon's blood, lake.

Yellow. Ochre, giallorino (Naples yellow), orpiment, risalgallo (realgar), zafferano (saffron), arzica.

Green. Verdeterra, verdeazzuro (copper green, malachite), verderame (verdigris).

White. (Chalk) bianco sangiovanni, (white lead) biacca.

Blue. Azzurro della magna (azurite), azzurro oltre marino (ultramarine).

Black. A soft black stone. Black made of the tendrils of young shoots of the vine. Black made of the skins of almonds, or the kernels of peaches. Lampblack.

Let us take these pigments in order, and consider them one by one.

Sinopia. This is one of the many names under which red ochres are mentioned, whether native or prepared by roasting yellow ochres. They have been used from the earliest times, and are perfectly reliable for all kinds of work. There is no need to dwell longer on them.

Cinabrese. This pigment is described by Cennino as being a mixture of red ochre with chalk. This is very commonly done now in order to prepare a bright red, and is a perfectly harmless practice.

Cinnabar (vermilion). This pigment is known in two forms, native and artificial. Cinnabar, or sulphide of mercury, is one of the commonest ores of that metal, and is occasionally found in pieces of a fine red colour when ground. Probably it was first used in this form. A much finer pigment is, however, obtained by subliming sulphur and mercury in a covered crucible, when the cinnabar is found at the top in crystalline masses.

The preparation of mercury is described by Theophrastus, 300 B.C., and the early alchemists, such as Geber, were familiar with many of the compounds of mercury, so that there can be little doubt that they were also familiar with the artificial preparation of vermilion.

The oldest of the manuscripts on the preparation of pigments, that at Lucca, supposed to be of the eighth century, describes the preparation of artificial vermilion; and similar recipes occur repeatedly in manuscripts of later dates. Returning again to Cennino, there can be no doubt that the vermilion he refers to is artificial. He says "*This colour is produced by alchemy, performed in an alembic . . . You may find many receipts, especially among the friars . . . Always purchase whole cinnabar . . . That which is convex on the top, and covered with needle-shaped filaments is the best*". It has been suggested more than once that the old masters used the native cinnabar, but on the whole the evidence is, I think, against this view. Evidently Cennino, at any rate, was familiar with the artificial variety.

No people have been more famous than the Chinese for the preparation of vermilion, and they still have a deservedly high reputation for it. It seems to have been used by them, from very early times, as a royal colour; and we find, according to Marco Polo, that the paper currency of Kublai Khan was stamped with the royal signature in vermilion. This remains the custom to the present day in China. The Chinese prepare the vermilion now by subliming sulphur and mercury, and then grinding, washing, and floating over. According to an account published in the *Chemical News*, the vermilion is suspended in water containing a little size. In this, it settles slowly, and the top layer is then removed. I have examined many samples of vermilion from China. It is a little difficult to get the genuine article, as most of that sent in here is merely European vermilion repacked in Chinese paper. The real article is unmistakable. It is not quite as bright as English vermilion, but is of a finer and softer colour, and is much more finely ground, being as soft as silk between the fingers. On subliming it, an ash is left, weighing from .1 to .05 per cent. or even less, of the whole. The ash is brown, and is apparently oxide of iron.

Unfortunately, English vermilion makers have departed from the ways of their forefathers. They prepare a product by heating the black sulphide of mercury with strong caustic potash, and the product is seldom free from alkali and alkaline sulphides.

Chinese vermilion may be safely mixed with white lead. I know a sample so mixed which has remained unchanged for forty years. I should not like to try the same experiment with many of the vermilions made here.

You will ask, is vermilion a permanent colour when properly prepared? This question is somewhat difficult to answer, but I will give you my view of the matter. In the first place, let us consider the facts before us. Vermilion is a sulphide of mercury. Now, this sulphide can exist in two varieties, the red, or vermilion, and a black sulphide. We can pass from the black to the red sulphide. We can also, unfortunately, pass very easily from the red to the black sulphide. If Chinese vermilion (that is practically the same article as Cennino describes) is ground in oil, painted out, and exposed to sunlight in a south window, it turns black in a few months. This agrees with Cennino's statement: *"But remember that vermilion is not durable when exposed to the air; it is more lasting on pictures than on walls, because, by long exposure to the air, it becomes black when applied to walls."*

Evidently then, Cennino distrusted this pigment, though I venture to differ with his reason for doing so. We know of too many pigments that are affected by air or moisture. The case of vermilion seems to be different from these. No chemical change is needed. The action of the sun's rays alone seems to rearrange the molecules into the black variety. In the experiments on water colours made by Captain Abney and Professor Russell, it was proved that while so many so-called fugitive colours were permanent in dry hydrogen, this did not save vermilion from turning black. Now, let us look at the evidence on the other side. I have already mentioned the experiment with vermilion in the late Holman Hunt's studio. But we can get other examples. There are many reds in the National Gallery that can only be produced by vermilion. Among others, the red in the "Rape of Helen" by Benozzo Gozzoli, 1420–98.

How, then, are these apparently contradictory facts to be reconciled? If we accept the theory put forward by Abney and Russell, that the rate of destruction of a pigment is a function of the amount of light falling on it, and that, consequently, a feeble light for one hundred years produces the same effect as a strong light for one year, we cannot reconcile these facts. But this opinion of theirs has not been accepted by the best authorities, such as Professor Church; nor does it agree with the experience of chemists in other directions. Let us take, for example, the action of heat in assisting chemical

E

change. There are some changes which take place at a gradually accelerating rate, as the temperature is raised, but there are others which do not begin appreciably until a certain temperature is passed. Vermilion is a case of this kind. It does not change in the diffused light of a room, but is quickly altered by direct sunlight. In this way only can I account for the facts before us. Under proper conditions, then, vermilion, properly made, is, I believe, a reliable pigment, and may be safely used. European vermilions, unless carefully washed with weak acid, and then with water, are not reliable. In this way, seventy per cent. of the ash is removed.

Minium or Red Lead. This pigment, prepared by the careful roasting of litharge, has been long known. It is described by Pliny, and, according to this authority, was discovered 320 B.C. There can be no doubt that this pigment has been much used in the past, and it is still very largely used for house-painter's work. It is, however, not used by artists, as it has fallen completely into discredit. To my mind, there is no more beautiful red, and I think it is a great loss to the palette. Two reasons for not using it are usually given. One, that it tends, like all lead pigments, to blacken in impure air. The other, that it is actually decomposed by daylight, returning to the dull brownish-yellow litharge. It is of interest here to note what Cennino Cennini says of it; *"This pigment is only proper to be used in pictures; for if it be used on walls, on exposure to the air it suddenly becomes black, and loses its colour."* It used to be customary to wash it before use with wine and water. More than one reference shows that it was not considered a very safe pigment. It is best prepared by roasting white lead. It is now, I believe, usually prepared from litharge. The minium prepared from white lead is a much finer pigment. While its use in pictures is doubtful, it can safely be used on illuminated manuscripts.

Amatisto. Cennino Cennini says it is a natural colour, and is produced from a hard, firm stone from which burnishing tools can be made. It is a purple colour, and is obviously hæmatite. One curious point is that Cennino Cennini says it is the colour that cardinals use. *"The cardinals had the red hat by a decree of the Council of Lyons, held in 1245 by Innocent IV. They did not adopt the red dress till 1464, that is, under the pontificate of Paul II; therefore at the period when Cennino was living, they still wore the purple colour".* (Tambroni).

Dragon's Blood. I have already referred to this resin. It is mentioned by

Pliny, and is the resin obtained from the calamus palm (*Pterocarpus Draco*, Linnæus. Dragon tree.). Cennino says of this pigment, "*Let it alone; it will never do you much credit*".

Lake, which comes next in order, I have already discussed.

Yellow Ochre. Nothing need be said about this pigment. A natural earth, it has been used from the earliest times, and is absolutely permanent. Cennino describes a very fine variety he found near Casole.

Giallorino. The history and nature of this pigment are somewhat obscure. Cennini distinctly states that it is a volcanic product. He states that it is not a brilliant yellow, though brighter than ochre, and never makes bright greens. Mrs Merrifield considers that several pigments were included under this name. I cannot do better than give her summing up of the matter.

"*A native mineral yellow pigment, known by the name of giallorino, giallorino di Napoli, jaune de Naples, luteolum Napolitanum.*"

This is doubtless the yellow referred to by Cennino. All trace of it seems to be lost, though probably a proper search in a volcanic district would lead to its discovery.

Mrs Merrifield then goes on: "*I consider it established that they used two kinds of Naples yellow, namely:*

1. A native mineral pigment found in the neighbourhood of volcanos, the nature of which is not accurately known, and which was called giallorino di Napoli and jaune de Naples, and which is synonymous with the first kind of giallorino above mentioned.

2. An artificial pigment now in use composed of the oxides of lead and antimony, called giallo di Napoli, jaune de Naples, and Naples yellow".

This compound of lead and antimony oxide has long been used as a pigment for glazing pottery and has been found in Babylonian bricks. I have prepared it and Mr Roberson gave me a sample of it. It is an excellent yellow.

Orpiment or Auripigmentum. This sulphide of arsenic exists both as a natural and artificial pigment. The natural sulphide is found in volcanic districts. It has not been found in any of the ancient Greek or Roman paintings. Cennino says it is unfit for use in distemper, because it turns black. He mentions it as being an artificial pigment. It was known and used through the best periods of art, but always with special precautions, as being liable to change and to attack other pigments.

Cornelius Jansen says: "*Orpiment will ly fayre on any colour except verdigris, but no colour can ly fayre on him; he kills them all*".

De Mayerne, speaking of Vandyck, says: "*He makes use of orpiment, which is the finest yellow that is to be found, but it dries very slowly, and, when mixed with other colours, it destroys them. In order to make it dry, a little ground glass should be mixed with it. In making use of it, it should be applied by itself, the drapery (for which alone it is fit) having been prepared with other yellows. Upon them, when dry, the lights should be painted with orpiment; your work will then be in the highest degree beautiful*".

This addition of powdered glass is advised by Cennino for another reason. It will be noted, from these accounts, that it does not seem liable to alter in itself, but to act on other colours. If it was liable to change, it would be advisable to use a different medium than oil. There can be no objection apparently to using it in the way stated, but it would not be safe to put it into the hands of a modern artist, as he would probably mix it too freely with other colours. The reason for not painting it over with verdigris I have already given.

Risalgallo Realgar, or Red Orpiment. This pigment, prepared by heating gently orpiment, has similar properties, and must be used with the same precautions.

Zafferano (Saffron). Cennino recommends preparing this colour by putting the saffron in a bag and rubbing it down with lye. He says it is good for staining linen or paper, and it makes a beautiful green with verdigris, but must not be exposed to the air. This is, of course, a very fugitive colour, and was probably only used for temporary purposes. Saffron was used for colouring varnishes.

Arzica. Cennino says that this pigment is not durable when exposed to the air, and is not to be used on walls. According to the Bolognese manuscript it is a lake prepared from weld (wild mignonette). It is probably the most permanent of the yellow lakes. When used for dyeing, weld yields a very beautiful yellow, which stands exposure to sunlight remarkably well, and is probably the most permanent yellow dye. It was used by William Morris for his tapestry work. At the same time the yellows in the old tapestries do not seem to bear exposure and time so well as the reds and blues. In many cases they are almost completely gone. So that Cennino's judgment of this pigment is probably correct.

This completes the list of yellow pigments mentioned by Cennino Cennini. He has, however, omitted one of the first importance from the list, to which he devotes a great part of his book, namely, gold. He describes elsewhere the grinding up of gold leaf for use in miniature painting, and, as his panels are laid on with gold, he depends on it for many of his effects. The use of gold as a yellow pigment, however, apart from decorative work, is common. Those who have not tried do not know what a wonderfully rich effect can be produced by the glazing over gold of transparent pigments.

Verde Terra (Terre Verte). There is no need to say anything about this natural earth. Like the ochres, it is useful and absolutely reliable, and always has and always will be used. Cennino says that it may be used instead of bole for preparing the surface of gold.

Verderame (Verdigris). Of this pigment Cennino says it is good in pictures tempered with glue, but must never be mixed with white lead. He also says it is improved in colour by grinding with vinegar, but is not durable.

This pigment was largely used apparently both by the Italian and Flemish painters. It was prepared by exposing plates of copper to the action of acetic acid vapour, and it is a subacetate of copper. I have dealt fully with this green in the former chapter. Probably its turning black as it seems to have done, in many old pictures, has been due to cleaning with alkaline soap.

Bianco Sangiovanni (Whiting). This is largely whiting, or chalk, and is recommended for fresco work by Cennino Cennini. His method of preparation is, however, a beautiful one. He takes slaked lime, and, mixing it with water, keeps it for eight days, changing the water every day. He then makes it into small cakes, and lets them dry in the sun. As he says, the older they are (that is, the more completely they change back into carbonate) the whiter they become.

Biacca (White Lead). Cennino says that it must not be used for fresco, as it turns black, but may be used on pictures. This pigment was known to the ancients, though not used on walls. It always has been, and still is, prepared (some of it) in the same way, by the action of vinegar vapour on metallic lead; a process popularly known as the Dutch process. There is no reason to suppose that the pigment made now by this process differs in any way from that used by the old masters. Under the name of flake white, it is used today for oil painting. It may be as well to explain, here and now, certain points about this pigment which seem to be not clearly understood by artists.

In the first place, it is necessary to understand that stack lead, as I shall call it, that is, white lead made by the action of acetic acid vapour on lead plates, contains two substances, one known as carbonate, the other hydrate of lead, and it owes its peculiar properties to the intimate union in the right proportion of these two. One of the most important of these properties is its power of combining with the oil to form what is known as a lead soap, thus forming a leathery substance of great durability. All the so-called permanent whites do not do this, and consequently remain merely a mixture of particles of pigment with the oil. Furthermore, a great deal of white lead is made now by a precipitation process. It is whiter than stack lead and, therefore, preferred by artists; but it does not combine with the oil, as stack lead does, and is not so reliable.

Now, to illustrate what I mean by this combining with the oil, I will describe an experiment I made. I coated some pieces of canvas with different whites, such as patent white, precipitated white lead, and so on, and fixed them up on a roof, where they would flap about in the wind and get all the weather going. The stack lead canvas was not affected by this treatment, but the other whites cracked and dusted off.

To go on to another point—the darkening of white lead. In impure air, containing certain compounds of sulphur, white lead turns to an unpleasant brown. If, however, it is then exposed to sunlight, it quickly recovers again and returns to its original white.

Besides this action, if kept in the dark it becomes of a yellow colour, not disagreeable. This is quite different from the effect of sulphuretted hydrogen, but can also be removed by exposure to sunlight.

The ease with which white lead is thus restored has not, I think, been allowed for sufficiently in considering its use as a pigment.

Azzurro della Magna (Azurite Mountain Blue). Cennino says it is found in the veins of silver mines, and that it comes from Germany and from Greece. There was, probably, no blue more universally used than this during the best periods of Italian art. I have already discussed its use in illuminated manuscripts and the dates when it replaced ultramarine. It is repeatedly referred to, and Professor Branchi of Pisa has found it in many old pictures and frescoes.

I do not doubt that the blue often seen on the walls of our cathedrals, where a little of the old colouring remains, is azurite. It is true that recipes for artificial copper blues are found in early manuscripts but I have never found it in use till after 1600. It was called "Blue Bice".

With reference to the use of copper blues in painting, however, a few remarks are necessary. In the first place, it seems to have been the practice to lay on this blue with size and not with oil, the opinion being that in oil it turned green. The turning green was due to the yellowing of the oil. Azurite is a weak stainer. In order to be able to use size in oil painting, the oil surface was rubbed with a little garlic. In this way, a sticky surface was formed on which the size could grip. The use of size in this way is undoubted, and has been found in restoring some ancient pictures. After laying on with size, it was varnished over in many cases. In fresco, of course, the blue cannot be used as it is acted on by lime.

We have discussed elsewhere the Egyptian Blue and the more modern smalt, apparently both unknown to Cennino Cennini.

They are difficult to use in oil, as fine grinding destroys their beauty, but are, I believe, especially applicable to fresco work. I know of no blue at present in the market which can be more safely recommended for fresco-painting, and I think that Egyptian Blue might well be revived for this purpose.

Azzurro oltre Marino (Ultramarine). We now come to the most famous of all blues, real ultramarine, prepared from lapis lazuli. Cennino says, *"Ultramarine is a colour more noble, beautiful and perfect than any other colour; and its good qualities exceed anything we can say in its favour."* The utmost pains used to be taken with its preparation from the stone, and it was always very expensive. Certain monasteries were famous for preparing it, and supplied it to the artists they employed; and many stories are told of their stingy ways with this colour, and how they suspected the artists of stealing it, and so on. It is still prepared, but has been replaced by the artificial ultramarines. These are similar in chemical composition, and very beautiful, and the best qualities seem durable. But it is very questionable if they equal in any way, the real article. I quote in full Cennino's description of the method of preparing this colour. It is very similar to the receipts given in other manuscripts. This blue is fully dealt with in my chapter on pigments.

"*Of the nature of azzurro oltre marino (ultramarine blue), and how it is prepared.*

"*Ultramarine blue is a colour noble, beautiful, and perfect beyond all other colours, and there is nothing that could be said of it but it will still exceed this (praise). On account of its great excellence I shall speak of it at length and give you full directions for preparing it; and you must pay great attention to them, that you may gain honour and service from them. And with this colour, together with gold (which adorns all the works of our art) let everything be resplendent, whether on walls or panels.*

"*First take some lapis lazuli; and if you would know how to distinguish the best stones, take those which contain most of the blue colour, for it is mixed with what is like ashes. That which contains least of this ash pigment is the best; but be careful that you do not mistake it for azzurro della magna, which is as beautiful to the eye as enamel.*

"*Pound it in a covered bronze mortar, that the powder may not fly away; then put it on your slab of porphyry, and grind it without water; afterwards take a covered strainer like that used by the druggists for sifting drugs (spices) and sift it, and pound again as much as is required. But bear in mind that the more you grind, the more finely powdered the azzurro will be, yet it will not be so beautiful and rich and deep in colour, and that the finely ground sort is fit for miniature painters, and for draperies inclining to white. When the powder is prepared, procure from the druggist six ounces of resin of the pine, three ounces of mastic, and three ounces of new wax to each pound of lapis lazuli. Put all these ingredients into a new pipkin and melt them together. Then take a piece of white linen and strain these things into a glazed basin. Then take a pound of the powder of lapis lazuli; mix it all well together into a paste, and that you may be able to handle the paste, take linseed oil, and keep your hands always well anointed with this oil. This paste must be kept at least three days and three nights, kneading it a little every day; and remember that you may keep it for fifteen days or a month, or as long as you please. When you extract the azure from the paste proceed thus: make two sticks of strong wood, neither too thick nor too thin, about a foot long; let them be well rounded at each end and well polished (smoothed). Then, your paste being in the glazed basin into which you first put it, add to it a porringer of lye, moderately warm; and with these two sticks one in each hand, turn and squeeze and knead the paste thoroughly, exactly in the manner that you would knead bread. When you see that the lye is thoroughly blue, pour it out into a glazed basin; take the same quantity of fresh lye, pour it over the paste, and work it with the sticks as before. When this lye is very blue, pour it into another glazed basin, and continue to do so for several days, until the paste no longer tinges the lye. Then throw it away; it is good for nothing. Range all the basins before you on a table in order, that is to say, the first, second, third, and fourth; then, beginning at the first, with your hand stir up the lye with the azure, which by its weight will have sunk to the bottom, and then you will know the depth of colour of the azure. Consider how many shades of the azure you will have, whether three, four, or six, or what number you please, always remembering that the first drawn extracts are the best, as the first basin is better than the second. And if you have eighteen basins of extract, and you wish to make three shades of azure, take the contents of six basins and mix them together; that will be one shade. Proceed in the same manner with the others. But remember if you have good lapis lazuli, the azure from the first two extracts is worth eight ducats the ounce. The last two extracts are worse than ashes—may your eyes therefore be experienced, so as not to spoil the good azure by mixing it with the bad; and each day remove the lye that the azure may dry. When it is quite dry, according to the sorts you have, put it into skins, bladders or purses, as may be most convenient, and take notice that if the lapis lazuli should not be very good, or if, after having ground it, the colour were not to turn out deep (violante) enough, I will tell you how to give it a little colour. Take a little pounded Kermes lake (grana) and a little verzino, but mind the verzino is grated or scraped with glass; and then boil them together with lye or a little roche alum. And when they boil, and you see that the colour is a perfect crimson, before you have withdrawn the azure from the porringer, but well dried from lye, add to it a little of this lake and verzino, and with your finger mix everything well together; and let them remain till dried, without sun, or fire, or wind. When dry, put it into a skin or purse, and rejoice in it, for it is good and perfect. And bear in mind that it is a rare gift how to make it well. You must know also that it is rather the art of maidens than of men to make it, because they remain continually in the house, and are more patient and their hands are more delicate. But beware of old women. When you use this azure, take as much as you want; and if you are going to work on light dresses, it must be ground a little on your usual stone. And if you want it for laying grounds, it must be very little worked on the stone and always with very clear water, the stone being well washed and clean. And if the azure should get soiled in any way, take a little lye or clean water, and put it into the vase, and stir them well together, changing it two or three times, when the blue will be quite clean. I shall not treat of its tempera, because I shall hereafter describe all the temperas proper for*

73

every colour to be used on pictures, on walls, on iron, on paper, on stone, or on glass."

The blacks mentioned by Cennino are four in number; black chalk, a black prepared by charring the young shoots of the vine; a black from almond skins or peach stones; and lamp black. Charcoal black gives a beautiful neutral grey with white lead and was used by Frans Hals.

It will be noticed that he mentions no browns. Browns, however, such as umber, were known and used.

Besides these colours, Cennino mentions indigo, and states that a fine green can be made by mixing it with orpiment. He probably, however, only means it to be used in miniature painting.

He also mentions lakes, and warns against the lake from dyers' clippings.

I have already referred to lakes from Indian stick lac, which is a resin in which the Coccus Lac insects are embedded. The stick lac is boiled with water and the extracted dye evaporated down and sold as a pigment and for dyeing. This pigment can hardly be described as a lake, but an excellent lake can be prepared from it.

Cennino Cennini, after warning us from using lakes made from shreds of cloth because they are fugitive, tells us to procure *"the lake which is made from gum, and is dry and transparent and granular, so that it almost appears to be an earth; it has a blood red colour"*; this might well be a description of the pigment obtained from the Coccus Lac, unless it is an allusion to the gum from the juice of ivy, which no one has been able to prepare.

Having thus gone through the list of pigments given by him, it is of some interest to refer again to those that he regarded as safe for use in fresco. These were sinopia, amatisto, yellow ochre, Naples yellow, verde terra, bianco sangiovanni, and black. No blue is mentioned; though elsewhere he talks of using indigo, which is difficult to understand. Of these colours one is wanting from the modern palette, namely, Naples yellow. There can be no doubt that as safe a palette can be selected from among modern pigments. As stated in Chapter VI, if blue copper frits are introduced again, or cobalt blue is used, with cobalt green and oxide of chromium green, a perfectly safe palette could be made up along with the earths given above.

After the fifteenth century smalt, a cobalt glass, was introduced about 1600. From about 1620 artificial copper blues and greens known as blue and green verditer or blue and green bice came into use. The recipes for these artificial copper blues are as old as the twelfth century but I have never found them on a manuscript or picture until this late date. They seem to have come into use to replace malachite and azurite, to both of which they are very inferior. They were, however, successfully used. For example, the dress in the portrait of Madame Pompadour painted by Watteau in the Edinburgh National Gallery is painted with blue bice.

Prussian blue was discovered in the eighteenth century and came into use about 1760. These are all the additional pigments before the dawn of modern chemistry.

Plate 2

CHAPTER VI

Painting with Yolk of Egg

BEFORE going on to consider in detail the use of yolk of egg as a medium for painting during the thirteenth, fourteenth and fifteenth centuries in Italy, it is necessary to realise what the tempera picture looked like when it was finished.

After a tempera picture was finished, it was varnished and this varnish has scaled off so that now we see these tempera pictures as they were before varnishing.

It is, therefore, necessary to know what the varnish was like; but unfortunately Eastlake and his followers have written about mediæval varnishes without going into the laboratory and testing these mediæval recipes, with the result that more nonsense has been written about mediæval varnishes than about any other part of our subject. I deal with this subject fully in my chapter on varnishes, but the reader may take it that until the introduction of spirits of turpentine in the sixteenth century, the mediæval varnish was thick, sticky and dark, and could only be used by warming it and then rubbing it with the hand over the warmed picture, forming a thick layer.

Professor Church in his book quotes an experiment which he made, preparing a varnish according to the mediæval method from juniper resin, which seems to have been the resin principally used in the Middle Ages. He found the varnish to be of a dark, warm colour and taking a picture painted in tempera and varnishing it with this varnish, found that it imparted "an agreeable warm tone to pictures painted in tempera". He tells us that when compared with the cold aspect of an old unvarnished Italian tempera picture, he obtained a glowing colour over the whole picture.

Our leading authority on tempera painting, Lady Herringham, would probably not have approved of this change in the appearance of the tempera picture which won Professor Church's admiration, her own tempera pictures being varnished with a thin coat of colourless mastic dissolved in spirits of turpentine.

I do not propose to discuss the question as to whether the tempera pictures as we now have them, are superior to the same pictures when they left the artists' studio in the fourteenth or fifteenth century, covered with a thick layer of a warm varnish. That they were quite different in appearance to the unvarnished picture is clear from Cennino Cennini's own statement.

In Chapter 155 he tells us how to varnish a picture and advises us to delay doing so as long as possible. He then goes on to say: *"Varnish is a strong liquor and gives great force (dimostrativo), and will be obeyed in everything, and annuls every other tempera. And suddenly as you spread it over the picture, the colours lose their natural strength and must obey the varnish, and their own tempera has no longer power to refresh them."*

He evidently wishes to minimise this change as much as he can by delaying varnishing and using as pale a varnish as he could get, but the fact remains that though the varnish did not soak into the painted surface, this layer of a medium of high refractive index would alter the colour scheme and give transparency to pigments that, without the varnish, would appear opaque. He tells us that if properly done the pigments afterwards would become more fresh and beautiful, thus agreeing with Professor Church's opinion and not with the æsthetic views of the modern tempera painters.

It must have been very difficult to distinguish between a tempera picture varnished wiht a mediæval varnish, and a picture painted by Van Eyck and his followers, with stand oil.

There is, therefore, no comparison between the tempera picture today, and the fourteenth- or fifteenth-century tempera picture, covered with a comparatively thick layer of warm mediæval varnish.

The following account of how to paint with yolk of egg is condensed from the *Book on the Art* by Cennino Cennini, from whom we have already made so many quotations. Any artist who is proposing to paint in tempera should obtain Lady Herringham's edition of Cennino Cennini with her useful additions, also the book by Dan Thompson on the carving and gilding of gesso, and the useful publications of the Tempera Society.

Cennino Cennini begins by describing three different kinds of glue (Chapter 109). The first glue is called *Colli di Spicchi*. It is made of the clippings of the muzzles of goats, feet sinews, and clippings of the skins. This glue would correspond very closely with the glue used by carpenters today. The second glue (Chapter 110) is made from the waste of sheep and goat parchment and from the clippings of this parchment. These are washed, soaked for the space of one day in water, and then boiled. This glue is used not only for mixing with gesso, but for painting with pigments where size is the best medium to use, and is also used as a thin wash over the egg painting when it is finished and before it is varnished. The third glue (Chapter 112) is made of cheese softened in water and then mixed with quick lime. This glue is used when it is necessary to cement boards together in order to make a large panel.

These recipes are very old and are to be found in the manuscript of Theophilus of the twelfth century.

A piece of well seasoned wood must be obtained for the panel, and he advises, if it is not well seasoned, to boil the panel first in water. He prefers poplar as the wood for the panel. The Italian panels are very thick, usually at least one inch. The painters of the North preferred thin panels of well seasoned oak. If there are any defects due to knots in the panel, they are filled up with a mixture of glue and sawdust, and the whole of the panel is covered with a coat of weak glue which, after it is dry, is covered with a coat of strong glue. Some old fine white linen cloth is then taken, torn into strips and glued over the surface of the panel. This undercoating of linen is readily detected on genuine fourteenth- and fifteenth-century pictures by an X-ray photograph.

The panel is now ready for the first coat of what is called *Gesso Grosso*, which is a mixture of plaster of Paris ground with glue, as you would grind colours, and spread over the surface with a large spatula. This is left to dry for three days and then rubbed with a rasp until smooth.

The second coat of gesso is prepared by mixing plaster of Paris thoroughly with a large quantity of water, and stirring up every day until it is completely slaked. The water is then thrown away. This *Gesso Sottile* is then made into cakes and allowed to dry. It is used as grounds for gilding, for working in relief, and other fine work.

This *Gesso Sottile* is soaked in water and ground with the muller. It is then mixed with some of the parchment glue, worked with the hand so that it is free from froth, warmed in a pipkin, placed in boiling water, and then spread with a large and very soft brush of hogs' bristles, rubbing with the fingers so as to incorporate it thoroughly with the first layer of gesso. Layer upon layer

F

of gesso is laid on with a brush across and across, each layer being allowed nearly to dry before a fresh coat is put on.

When it is thoroughly dry, powdered charcoal is sifted over the whole surface and spread equally over the whole ground, with a hen's feather. It is then rubbed with a smooth iron and then dusted off, leaving the ground as white as milk.

If the panel is to be gilded, Cennino Cennini mentions three mordants that can be used. One prepared from white of egg and Armenian bole, one a quick drying oil varnish, similar to the gold size we now use, and one from garlic juice. His methods of gilding and burnishing do not differ in any way from modern practice, so that I do not propose to quote them here. Besides mentioning gilding with gold, he also describes the laying on of tin foil which was sometimes used in place of gold, being covered with a yellow varnish similar to the Spanish leather hangings. I have been able to reproduce these effects by coating a canvas with size, then with gold size and tin foil, and then polishing the tin foil and varnishing it with an oil varnish coloured with dragon's blood.

Curiously enough, Cennino Cennini, having devoted all this time to the preparation of a panel on which to paint, does not tell us how the painting with yolk of egg is to be done. The pigments, he tells us, are all to be ground in water and kept in little closed vessels, and when they have settled, the water on the top poured off. These pigments are to be mixed in their wet condition with yolk of egg, but he does not tell us how much yolk of egg to use. I shall quote here, therefore, the proportions between pigment, water and yolk, given by an artist who has devoted his whole life to painting in tempera, John Duncan, R.S.A. After having laid the *Gesso Sottile*, he polishes it with an agate, and then coats it with two or three coats of weak size. He adds to each yolk of egg two eggspoonfuls of water, strains the whole through muslin, and to every two eggs adds one eggspoonful of a three per cent. solution of acetic acid, to prevent the yolk of egg going bad. Equal volumes of egg and pasty pigment are ground together on the muller. Some pigments, like terre verte and yellow ochre, require a little more egg. If a little of the pigment and its egg medium is painted out on glass and left to dry, next day it should be possible to remove it with a spatula, as a leathery film. If it is powdery, enough egg has not been added. Each layer of pigment, when dry, can be polished with a piece of soft linen rag giving an eggshell gloss.

I owe to Mr Tudor Hart the following method of obtaining the yolk as free as possible from the white. He rolls the yolk gently, passing it from one palm to another and wiping the free palm clean between each change. Pinching the enclosing skin of the yolk between the thumb and finger and lifting it gently from the palm of the hand, he punctures the yolk skin with a fine pointed blade, and lets the yolk run out.

The finished tempera picture may require a thin coating of size before it is varnished. Cennino Cennini advises keeping it for a year before the varnishing is done, he then warms the surface of the picture by placing it in the sun, warms the thick sticky dark coloured oil varnish, and rubs it over the picture with his hand.

The yolk of egg is an emulsion of albumen and oil with an emulsifying agent. The albumen sets and, ultimately, the oil medium, behaving like a drying oil, the whole forming a very durable binding medium.

The paint has to be laid on in very thin layers, each layer having time to dry. A series of tints, let us say, are made up according to the old Byzantine practice, laid side by side and blended where they meet. Under flesh a thin layer of terre verte is laid. As we shall see later on, the picture is first laid out in chiaroscuro.

Plate 3

PLATE 3   VIRGIN AND CHILD

by Hans Memling

Nelson Atkins Gallery, Kansas City

Oil, painted about 1460

CHAPTER VII

Painting in Drying Oil

BEFORE proceeding to investigate the nature of the oil medium as used in the fourteenth century, and as employed by Van Eyck, it is necessary to clear our minds of the statements made by Vasari on this subject.

Vasari, while an excellent story-teller, was evidently ignorant of the technique of oil painting before his time, and can never have read the *Book of the Art* by Cennino Cennini, although he refers to that painter. He is responsible for the suggestion that Van Eyck discovered a new medium, although he quite evidently does not understand what it was. He attributes the invention first to one brother, then to the other. All suggestions that Van Eyck made a discovery are found to be derived from Vasari.

We possess, fortunately, a copy of the inscription on Van Eyck's tombstone, in which he is described as a great painter, but there is no suggestion that he introduced or made a new discovery in connection with painting in oil. Moreover it is quite obvious if we examine Van Eyck's pictures, that they do not represent the efforts of a man fumbling with a new medium, but are the final triumph in the hands of a master of a long known and thoroughly understood technique.

To begin at the beginning, the first account of the use of oil was as a varnish. The physician Aetius of the fifth century describes how to prepare linseed oil and tells us that walnut oil can be used as a varnish. This is the earliest mention of the properties of a "drying" oil.

The next mention of the making of oil varnishes is given in the Lucca manuscript. This is the first important manuscript connecting the classical with the mediæval period, and is in the library of the Cathedral at Lucca. It is supposed to be of about the eighth century and deals with painting. There is a list of pigments similar to those given by Pliny, but giving in addition a recipe for the preparation of vermilion by subliming together sulphur and mercury.

There are also recipes for the making of oil varnishes. At the end of the list of pigments, there is the following Latin phrase:

"*Ita memoramus omnium operationes quae in parietibus simplice in ligno cere commixtis coloribus in pellibus ictiocollon commixtum.*" "*Thus we mention operations with all of them, on walls unmixed, on wood the colours being mixed with wax, on skins fish-glue being mixed.*"

Professor Berger, in quoting this passage leaves out the first "in", thus altering the whole meaning of the passage. Surprised at this, I wrote to Lady Herringham, who told me that she had a photograph of the actual manuscript in which "in" was repeated three times. Evidently in the eighth century, buon fresco was used for painting on walls and wax for painting on panels. This is the last mention of wax as a medium. The experts employed in cleaning the ikons in Russia told me that they found them painted in wax up to about A.D. 600, then in tempera.

After the Lucca manuscript, which connects the classical with the mediæval period, the next most important record that we have of the artistic crafts of the twelfth century are the *Schedula* by Theophilus Presbyter, an unknown monk. Several copies of this manuscript have been discovered in various libraries.

It treats of painting on walls, on panels and in books; of work in glass, for vessels, windows, and mosaics; of work in metals, gold, silver, bronze, and iron; of musical instruments; and of many incidental and allied operations.

A complete account of these various manuscripts and their editors and translators will be found in the *Speculum*, a journal of mediæval studies published by the Mediæval Academy of America, Cambridge, Mass. The article is by D. V. Thompson, published in Vol. VII, April 1932. No. 2.

The main interest of the *Schedula* to us is that for the first time linseed oil is mentioned as a medium for painting.

He tells how to express linseed oil from its seed, and how to use it as a painting medium. The following are quotations from the manuscript of Theophilus, on this subject. Chapter XX. "*Of reddening doors and of linseed oil.*

"*If, however, you wish to redden panels, take linseed oil, which you make in this manner: Take linseed and dry it in a pan over the fire, without water. Then put it into a mortar and bruise it with the pestle until it becomes a very fine powder; placing it again in the pan, and pouring a little water upon it, make it thus very hot. After-wards fold it in a new cloth and place it in the press, in which olive, or walnut, or poppy oil is accustomed to be expressed, that this also may be expressed in the same manner. With this oil grind minium, or cinnabar, upon the stone, without water, and paint over the doors or tablets, which you wish to redden, with a pencil, and you will dry them in the sun. Then paint them again, and again dry them. At last cover them over with that gluten which is called varnish, and which is made in this manner."*

This method of expressing the linseed oil agrees with modern practice, but no account is given of how to refine it or how to convert it into a drying oil. Such an unrefined oil would dry rather slowly, and the painting would therefore be the better for exposure to the sun.

In the two following chapters two recipes are given for making varnishes. These recipes will have to be considered more fully elsewhere.

Chapter XXVII. *"Of colours ground with oil and gum.*

"All sorts of colours can be ground and laid upon woodwork, with the same kind of oil, in those things only which can be dried in the sun; because each time that you have laid on one colour, you cannot superpose another upon it until the first has dried, which, for figures, is excessively long and tedious. If, however, you wish to hasten your work, take gum which exudes from the cherry or plum tree, and cutting it up very small, place it in an earthenware pot, and pour water upon it abundantly and place it in the sun, or in the winter upon the coals, until the gum has liquified; and mix it together with a smooth piece of wood. Then strain it through a cloth, and grind the colours with it and lay them on. All colours and their mixtures can be ground and laid on with this kind of oil, except minium and ceruse and carmine, which are ground laid on with white of egg. Spanish green is not mixed with sussus under the gluten, but it is laid on by itself with gum gluten. You can otherwise mix it if you wish it."

It is of interest to note in passing that Theophilus makes no mention of using yolk of egg to paint pictures.

It is evident from this account that he knew how to prepare the raw oil, but there is no suggestion of subsequent treatment.

If we turn to the manuscript of Eraclius, which is of about the same date, we find a recipe for preparing oil for tempering colours. He heats the oil with a little lime, which, unless the addition of lime was very small, would prove injurious, and then adds ceruse and puts the oil in the sun, stirring frequently. This treatment would result in giving him an excellent drying oil, as the solution of lead compounds in linseed oil results in enabling them to dry quickly, and I have myself prepared an excellent drying oil on these lines.

A later recipe found in the Strasbourg manuscript boils the oil with calcined bones and white vitriol. I find that if linseed oil is boiled with calcined bones, some two per cent. or three per cent. is dissolved as a linoliate, which has no perceptible effect on the oil. White vitriol (sulphate of zinc) if ignited so as to drive off the water, might remove water dissolved in the oil, and if it was an impure sulphate of zinc containing manganese, it might act as a dryer, but the whole recipe does not give us much more information than we had before.

Besides these recipes, in the manuscript of Petrus D. S. Audemar, not later than the thirteenth century, several references are made to the use of oil as a painting medium, but the mention of these recipes and the use of oil as a painting medium, is not the main proof that it had entered into common use long before the time of Van Eyck. There is a remarkable series of accounts existing in England in connection with the painting both at Westminster and at Ely Cathedral of the thirteenth and fourteenth century, showing that large quantities of linseed oil were bought for the decorations of these buildings. These accounts refer, in many cases, to the painted chamber at Westminster, and show that it was customary to buy oil and both red and white varnish.

There are also other records of painting in oil. For instance, in 1351–52, there are records in the archives at Bruges of painting in oil done in the chapel of the Town Hall.

When we go to Italy, we find that the use of oil was known in the fourteenth century, as Eastlake tells us that on examining fourteenth-century tempera pictures, he found distinct indications of the use of oil for certain parts of the picture. We may take it, therefore, as established, that when Van Eyck set to work to paint a picture he had one hundred and fifty years, at least, of tradition behind him.

The next question we have to ask ourselves, is how this oil was prepared for use by the painter. The artist today has his pigments ground in a purified raw oil, but the practice was very different in the fourteenth century, as we

Plate 4

I have reproduced a copy of the signature on this portrait made for me by a skilful sign writer.

The white head-dress worn by Arnolfini's wife is a perfect example of painting in Stand Oil, showing the smooth flow of the paint and the absolute sharpness of the lines where they meet the paint of the rest of the picture.

find by referring to Cennino Cennini. He tells us how to prepare an oil for painting pictures and for painting on walls. His two recipes for this purpose are as follows:

Chapter 91. "*How to make oil fit for tempering colours, and also for mordants, by boiling over the fire.*

"*It will be very useful to you to know how to prepare this oil, for many things that are done; therefore, take one, two, three, or four pounds of linseed oil, and put it into a new pipkin; if it is glazed, so much the better. Make a small furnace, and make a round hole, into which the pipkin fits exactly, so that the flame may not reach it, because the fire easily catches it, and there would be danger to the oil, and also of burning the house. When you have made your furnace, put a moderate fire in it; and the more slowly your oil boils, the better and more perfect it will be. Let it boil until it is reduced to half the quantity. But to prepare mordants, when it is reduced to half the quantity, add to each pound of oil one ounce of liquid varnish (vernice liquida) and let it be very fine and clear: and oil thus prepared is good for mordants.*"

Chapter 92. "*How to prepare good and perfect oil by cooking it in the sun.*

"*When you have prepared this oil (which is also cooked in another way, better for painting, but not for mordants, for which it must be done on the fire, that is, cooked), take your linseed oil, and in summer time put it in a basin of bronze or copper. And in August (quando e il sole leone) place it in the sun; and if you keep it there till it is half wasted, it will be exactly right for mixing with colours. And you must know that, in Florence, I have found the finest and best that there can be.*"

Chapter 93. "*How to grind colours in oil and to use them on walls.*

"*Let us return to grinding the colours. Begin and grind colour by colour, as you did when working in fresco, except that where you then ground them with water, you must now grind them with oil. And when you have ground them, that is to say, all the colours (for every colour can be mixed with oil except bianco sangiovanni), provide small vessels, either of lead or of tin, into which put these colours. And if you cannot find such, get glazed vessels, and put the ground colours into them; put them in a box, that they may keep clean. When you would paint a drapery with three gradations of colour, as I have previously taught you, divide the space, and let each colour be laid in its proper place with a miniver brush, uniting one colour well with another, the colours being very stiff. Then stop for a few days and return again to your work, see how the paint covers, and repaint where necessary. And in this way paint flesh or anything you please; and in this way mountains, trees, and every other work. Provide a vessel of tin or lead (something like a lamp), about the height of your finger, half fill it with oil, and keep your brushes in it that they may not dry".*

The most significant words are "with a miniver brush", that is with a brush made from the hairs of the grey squirrel, which are even more pliable than sable. We shall find the significance of this choice of a soft pliable brush presently.

One method of preparing an oil for painting, he tells us, is by boiling the oil until it has reached half its volume (Chapter 91). The other method is by exposing the oil to the sun until it is half wasted. In both cases we get a thick and sticky oil. It is, therefore, evident that he does not regard a thin oil as suitable for painting, but gets it into a thick and sticky condition before using it. Eastlake, being accustomed to only one method of painting in oil, in his *Material for a history of Oil Painting*, assumes that the use of this thick and sticky oil meant that all painting with it would be very coarse. It never seems to have occurred to him that by using raw oil the artists of the fourteenth century would have the painting medium which is used today, and they must have had some reason for using a thick and sticky medium.

Before considering why they selected such a medium, it is necessary to state what the effect on linseed oil is on these two methods of treatment. The result of exposure to the sun is to produce a thick and sticky oil by partial oxidisation. The result of the boiling of the oil is to produce a more profound change. The oil is partially decomposed, but the main change is the joining of the linseed oil molecules into large aggregates. The resulting oil is called stand oil, has long been manufactured in Holland, and is also manufactured in this country. It was doubtless made among other purposes for the manufacture of printing ink. Before printing with movable type was invented, playing cards were printed from engraved wooden blocks for which a printing ink was required, and in order to prepare a printing ink, it is necessary to use stand oil. So quite apart from its being used for other purposes, it must have been manufactured in the fourteenth and fifteenth centuries for printing. Today it is used for grinding lithographic colours and for the making of enamel paints. It has two peculiar properties. If we use it to paint with, a perfectly sharp edge is obtained, much sharper than is possible with a pigment ground in raw oil, but within the area covered by the paint, the oil

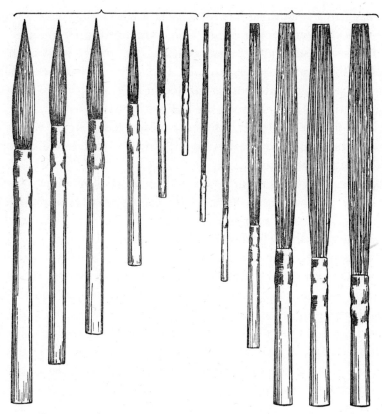

FIG. 2. The brushes used by sign-writers (actual size) from
Winsor & Newton's catalogue

FIG. 3. Copy of the Van Eyck signature by a sign-writer,
painted with lamp black ground in stand oil

flows of itself to a smooth surface which dries with a shine like a varnish, a peculiarity of the Van Eyck medium which was noticed by Vasari.

One day I was discussing with an artist the question of what medium was used by Van Eyck, when he said to me, "I am satisfied that the signature on the Arnolfini portrait could not be painted in oil".

As the painting of a signature is the business of a sign-writer, I decided to find out something of his craft. I found a clever young sign-writer and discovered that their method of painting with oil is completely different from that of the painter of pictures.

The painter of pictures requires for his work a slick medium of the consistency of vaseline and uses a hard brush. The sign-writer uses a *thick sticky* medium and a *soft camel's hair* brush. *The sticky medium guides the brush.* I reproduce here a drawing of sign-writer brushes of actual size. I direct the attention of the reader to the long brush made up of a few camel's hairs. The sign-writer having put a little of his sticky paint on the end of this brush, can with one movement of the hand, draw a straight line of equal thickness and even distribution of paint.

I showed the young sign-writer some stand oil and he said, "That is just the medium I like". I gave him a photograph, full size, of the Van Eyck signature and some stand oil and asked him to grind some lamp black into the stand oil and paint a copy of the signature. I reproduce his copy here as an illustration.

I took him to the National Gallery in order to show him the Arnolfini picture and examine it with a magnifying glass. He was immensely interested and recognised it at once as the work of a sign-writer using his sticky medium.

Turning again to Eastlake, we find he is convinced that the painting medium used in the fourteenth century was a thick sticky oil, but he argues from that, that the painting must have been coarse. If he had studied the sign-writer's craft, he would have realised that a thick sticky medium made it possible to do much finer work than can be done with raw oil.

There can be no question that the sign-writer has preserved through the centuries the technical method of Van Eyck and his followers.

The interesting question arises where Van Eyck learnt his craft. England seems to have been one of the most important centres of painting in the thirteenth and fourteenth centuries, and we know that the contact between England and Flanders was very close, and Flemish painters were employed in the decoration of Ely and Westminster. It is possible, therefore, that Van Eyck was trained over here. He suddenly appears in the Netherlands, a man of nearly middle age, who is a master of painting. We know nothing about him before that except a possible place of birth. There can be no question that far from beginning to experiment on a new technique, he is the final and supreme master of a technique which had been developing in the North of Europe for at least one hundred years. It is not without interest that we owe the painting of Van Eyck and the art of printing both to Northern Europe, each of them requiring the same oil medium, stand oil. I suggest to the young student of the history of art, that we want a fresh enquiry into Northern paintings before 1400 to see how many of them are painted in oil. They have, in the lower room of the Berlin Gallery, a large number of pictures supposed to have been painted before 1400, all of which are lumped together as painted in tempera because of the obsession on the part of Directors of Art Galleries, an obsession for which we must blame Vasari, that all painting before Van Eyck was tempera. Eastlake states that he examined many Italian fourteenth-century pictures, and found that they had been partly painted in oil. This statement of his requires verification. It would also be of interest to decide whether the Italian painters ever actually adopted the Van Eyck technique or modified it to suit their own purpose. By the time of Vasari it is evident that all trace of the Van Eyck technique had been lost. This discovery of the way in which Van Eyck painted his pictures and the mediums that he used, far from closing the door of research, opens widely the door for a fresh enquiry into oil painting before 1400 and into Italian oil painting in the latter years of the fifteenth century.

It is obvious that Cennino Cennini must have been familiar with the properties of the thickened oil and its use as a medium. His reference to using a *miniver brush* shows his familiarity with the process.

A very interesting example of the use of stand oil is to be found in a picture called *The Bird Trap*, by Pieter Breughel the Elder.

This picture was exhibited at the Flemish Exhibition in the Royal Academy London, and a distinguished art critic rightly praised the picture as an excellent example of Breughel's work, but shortly after condemned it as a forgery.

Dr. Delporte, the owner of the picture, therefore asked me to make a thorough examination.

The background is very thinly painted on a gesso panel which has cracked in the characteristic manner. The trees and figures skating have been painted in evidently with stand oil, the paint lying in thick rounded ridges with sharp edges where it meets the under painting.

The art critic had assumed the picture to be a forgery because to the eye the cracks in the gesso seemed to stop abruptly at the edge of the paint of the trees and figures.

Under the microscope it was seen that the cracks passed right through the trunks of the trees but owing to the elasticity of the stand oil they were only visible under strong magnification. The critic had been deceived by these cracks not being visible to the eye.

Even the photograph reveals the sharp line where the stand oil used in painting the trunks of the trees meets the thin underpainting. Doubtless the trees were laid in with the point of a fine soft brush, the stand oil flowing to a smooth rounded surface. The fine painting of the branches shows the hand of a master of the sign-painter's method of painting.

The introduction of oil or spirits of turpentine, a volatile medium which could be mixed with oil, must have had a marked effect on the technique of the painter in oil. Yet Vasari makes no mention of it, and we owe to the de Mayern manuscript the information that Rubens painted with linseed oil dipping his brush into spirits of turpentine.

The introduction of spirits of turpentine, spike oil and rectified petroleum depended upon the art of distillation being developed. In the time of Pliny a crude distilled product from wood tar was obtained by heating the tar in a vessel, the mouth of which was closed with fleece, which was removed and wrung out at intervals, but Pliny does not suggest that this crude material was used for purposes of painting. The invention of a still, that is a closed vessel with a pipe leading out of it to a condenser, was first described by a learned lady called Cleopatra who lived in Egypt in the third century A.D., and in a manuscript in the library of San Marco there are drawings of stills which correspond to her description. The alchemists were therefore familiar with distillation for many centuries, and the distillation of alcohol from fermented spirits was carried out by an alchemist in the twelfth century; but that does not mean that distillation was used for commercial purposes; it is not until about the middle of the fifteenth century that aqua vitæ became a commercial article.

Evidently distillation was used for other purposes and consequently we find in the sixteenth century *Secreti* recipes for making varnishes by dissolving the softer resins in spirits of turpentine, spike oil and rectified petroleum.

The oleo-resins of the silver fir and of the larch exude from the trees in semi-solution in the volatile terpenes. If heated in a still in a current of steam the terpenes distil over, giving us spirits of turpentine.

Evidently, then, spirits of turpentine was not an article of commerce till late in the fifteenth century.

The earliest date that I have found for the use of spirits of turpentine is between the years 1465 and 1482. There is an illuminated manuscript in the Advocates' Library at Edinburgh, *Speculum Vitæ Christi*, known to have been painted between those two dates. I have already referred to it as containing a madder lake. It is partly painted in beeswax, which is laid on so thinly that it must have been emulsified in spirits of turpentine. We may take that as the earliest known date for the use of spirits of turpentine.

I shall now discuss fully the method of painting in the fifteenth century by laying in on the panel a finished picture in chiaroscuro, probably using lamp black mixed with size. It is possible that when turpentine came in this first painting might have been laid in with the oil pigments very much diluted with turpentine.

Plate 5

G*

PLATE 5   THE BIRD TRAP

by Pieter Breughel the Elder

Property of Dr. Delporte, Brussels

This picture is of great interest as it shows the use of Stand Oil in a new way. The whole landscape is thinly painted except the figures and trees which are laid in in Stand Oil. This is obvious on examining under the microscope. The result is a very unusual decorative effect.

CHAPTER VIII

The Building up of a Painting in the Fourteenth and Fifteenth Centuries

WE HAVE discussed fully the medium used by Van Eyck and his followers, an oil which made possible the high finish and detail which had been attained by the painters in egg and the illuminators of manuscripts.

We have next to study their method of building up a picture, which seems to have been followed both by oil and egg painters. Cennino Cennini (Chap. 122) describes how a picture should be begun. He tells us first to draw in the outlines of the design with charcoal. When the painter is satisfied with his design, he brushes away the charcoal, leaving just a faint indication, and draws in the outline with a pointed miniver brush and ink. Then he tells us, *"With some more of the ink and a flat pointed miniver brush, shade any folds and any shaded part of the face and you will have made an agreeable design which will cause all men to fall in love with your works"*.

The nature of the ink used by him is not stated. Both an ink made with lamp black and size, and an ink made with sulphate of iron and tannic acid, are mentioned in old manuscripts. Judging by the condition of a partly finished picture, it is obvious that a tannic acid ink was *not* used, or it would have faded to a faint brown. It is, therefore, clear that the ink used consisted of lamp black ground in size, thus corresponding to what we call Indian ink, which is of Chinese origin, and we are all familiar with the delicate work done in this medium by Chinese artists.

If, then, Cennino Cennini is correct, the chiaroscuro of a picture, whether to be finished in tempera or in oil, was first laid in in tempera.

Van Mander, writing in 1604, about the methods of the early painters in oil, gives us a similar account, telling us that the pictures were completely finished in chiaroscuro before being painted with oil colours.

Fortunately, we have three unfinished pictures in this country, one by Cima da Conegliano in the Edinburgh National Gallery, and two by Michelangelo in the National Gallery, London, and there is, in addition, the Santa Barbara by Van Eyck, in the Antwerp Gallery.

In all these pictures the first treatment has been to paint in tempera. In the Entombment (No. 790) by Michelangelo, the St John on the right supporting the Body of Christ has been painted in in red, ready for the final glazing with lake in oil. In the Madonna and Child (No. 809) the Madonna has been completely shaded in black and white, ready for the painting of blue, while the flesh of the two figures on the right has been thinly painted with terre verte, according to Cennino Cennini's directions. The picture by Cima is very interesting. The blue of the sky has already been laid in with tempera and then a cloud laid in over part of it in oil, the brush having been dragged, so as to reveal in places the underlying blue, below the grey of the cloud. The Santa Barbara has been completely finished in black and white, while the blue of the sky has been laid in at the top of the picture.

It is evident from these four pictures that the painters of that time did not limit themselves to chiaroscuro, but occasionally laid in with tempera a foundation colour, on which final oil or tempera colour was to be laid.

Unfortunately, these pictures are not dated. I am, therefore, assuming that this method of painting a picture had gone out when Vasari wrote his book, which was published in 1550, because he makes no mention of it, but tells us to grind pigments in raw oil and lay them direct on the primed canvas.

The painting in with tempera of the blue sky in the picture by Cima da Conegliano, and the strip of blue at the top of the unfinished Van Eyck, Santa Barbara, are of interest, as Cennino Cennini advises using size for the medium in the case of azurite, for the reason, already discussed, that this pigment is so sensitive to the yellowing of oil.

We have learnt to regard Vasari as quite unreliable in his account of the introduction of oil as a medium into Italy, but he may be right in his statement that Antonello da Messina, having studied under Van Eyck, first introduced the Van Eyck technique into Italy.

On visiting the National Gallery recently, I found that a portrait (No. 1141) by Antonello had been hung next the Arnolfini portrait by Van Eyck. I spent some time in examining the brushwork of both pictures through a powerful magnifying glass and have no hesitation in saying that the two pictures were painted with the same medium and with the same technique. The fourteenth-century Italian painter was quite familiar with the properties of a drying oil, and used it for glazing colour over gold. Its use instead of egg as a medium seems to have come into Italy about the middle of the fifteenth century, and from then onwards we find some painters painting in egg and others in oil. To take an example, the pictures by Crivelli are obviously painted in egg, and he was painting from about 1450 to 1495. On the other hand the pictures by Gentile and Giovanni Bellini are obviously in oil with one or two exceptions, and they were painting during the same period. It is interesting to find that the two techniques were so similar that in a large number of cases the National Gallery experts are unable to say whether a picture is painted in egg or oil. There is one indication which can be observed with a powerful magnifying glass. It is evident that the drawing of the figures was completed in black and white and thinly tinted with flesh colour, while the draperies were painted in with strong colour, thinly laid on if painted in egg, but much more thickly laid on if painted in oil. This is clearly shown in the photomicrograph of the infant's foot in the Ansidei Madonna by Raphael, where the thick layer of oil paint can be seen coming up against the thin delicate painting of the foot.

In trying to decide whether a picture has been painted in egg or in oil, we must keep in mind another possibility. Apparently the varnish used by the tempera painters has scaled off or been removed, and it has been the fashion in recent times to put a very thin coat of mastic over them, leaving them with the colouring and texture of the egg paint. It is highly probable that in the case of egg pictures which have passed through the hands of picture cleaners in the eighteenth and early nineteenth centuries, they were covered with a heavy oil varnish, making it difficult to distinguish them from oil pictures, without an examination.

A tempera painter carried out for me some experiments on painting in egg to which a few drops of oil or varnish had been added. This is a much more facile medium than egg alone and may have been the practice of the later tempera painters. It is also evident that the Italian painters when they began to use oil used a much more fluid oil than that used by Van Eyck and his school, raw oil gradually replacing the use of stand oil. Doubtless the oil merchant supplied the type of oil required by the artist and this is the reason why Vasari who used a raw oil had no knowledge of the nature of the oil used by Van Eyck.

The whole question of the introduction of oil could only be settled by a scientific examination of the pictures of the Italian school of the fifteenth century.

Plate 6

PLATE 6   SANTA BARBARA

Unfinished picture by Jan Van Eyck   Antwerp Museum

We have here a perfect example of the first stage of building up a picture as a complete drawing in black and white, the white being the gesso panel.

This drawing by Van Eyck is quite complete as a study in black and white, and there is a strip of blue along the top of the picture showing that the subsequent colouring has just been begun.

Plate 7

PLATE 7   MADONNA ENTHRONED

Unfinished picture by Cima da Conegliano

National Gallery of Scotland No. 1190

It is impossible to convey the full interest of this picture in a photograph. It is necessary to examine it both under the magnifying glass and under the microscope.

The greater part is in tempera but the laying on of oil paint has been begun. The blue sky has already been laid in with tempera, and a grey cloud has been painted in oil over the blue sky, as can be seen in the photograph. On examining this grey cloud through the microscope, we see the crystals of blue paint showing through the oil paint in the valleys left by the brush strokes, thus proving that the picture has been built up in the way I have described in the text, by painting in tempera and then laying oil paint over it.

Plate 8

Unfinished picture by Michelangelo

National Gallery 790

This picture is of interest because the robe on the figure of St. John has already been laid in with red paint, ready for the final glazing with a lake, as described in the text.

Plate 9

PLATE 9   MADONNA AND CHILD

Unfinished picture by Michelangelo

National Gallery 809

We have here a picture which has been completed in black and white except for the figures to the left. The flesh of these figures has already been laid over with a thin coating of terre verte according to Cennino Cennini's directions.

CHAPTER IX

Light

IN the course of our former chapters, we have not discussed the principle which was fully realised by the painters in fresco, tempera and oil, of the necessity for painting thinly on a white surface. The importance of this was gradually forgotten by the painters in oil and it is only necessary to walk quickly through the galleries of an Art Museum, taking them in their chronological order, to realise that we pass from brightly luminous pictures to pictures of a darker and darker gloom.

The pictures in tempera excel in this brightness of colouring, which no doubt has been assisted by the scaling off of the varnish with which they were originally covered, so that they are reflecting light and colour much more brilliantly today than when they left the artist's studio. We have seen that it was the practice both of oil and tempera painters to cover a panel with a gesso either consisting of plaster of Paris and size or of whitening and size. This covering of gesso forms a permanently white and brilliant background. Size, where not exposed to damp, has proved to be a very permanent organic binder and can be extracted practically unaltered from the coffin lids in Egyptian tombs. No chemical alteration takes place in plaster of Paris, and whitening, if not directly attacked by acid fumes, proves very permanent.

Just as a water-colour painter uses his white paper for his high lights so the early painter both in tempera and in oil, in his preliminary drawing of his picture in black and white, shaded with black on the white unchanging gesso. This might be subsequently covered up. Van Eyck freely uses white lead, but below all surface painting we have the original permanent division into white, which will not change, and black. If we compare the translucency of pigments in a medium like oil, we shall find it doubtful if we can regard even the most opaque pigments when finely ground as not slightly translucent. White lead itself consists of transparent crystals and owes its whiteness, like the whiteness of snow, to innumerable internal reflections. Some of the pigments used by the old masters, such as azurite and smalt, consist of transparent crystals in the one case, and transparent particles of glass in the other, and consequently they found considerable difficulty in using them in a medium like oil. While they used tempera medium such as size and egg, the difficulty of the lowering of brilliancy by a mixture with a medium of high refractive index like oil, did not so much occur. This matter of refractive index of a medium is not easy for an artist to understand. Supposing, for instance, I take powdered glass; it will appear as a white powder while it is in air, but as soon as I pour water on it, it becomes almost invisible because of the high refractive index of water, light being no longer reflected from it as before, but passing through it instead.

Oil has three defects as a medium. In the first place, it has a high refractive index; in the second place, it turns yellow with age; in the third place, the oil film gradually rises in refractive index with age; thus making all pigments ground in it more translucent, and lowering the whiteness and the opacity of white lead, while yellow pigments move towards the orange.

This is the cause of what is called *pentementa* in pictures; owing to the rise of refractive index in the oil, the surfaces of pigments become more translucent and under-painting begins to show through.

Suppose that I paint out a panel in black and white squares, and then when it is dry, coat it with white lead until the black and white squares are invisible. In the course of a year or two, the black and white squares will be showing again owing to the increased translucency of the white lead which is due to the rise in the refractive index in the oil. These difficulties do not occur with an egg medium, as the refractive index remains the same throughout the centuries. As I have already stated about stand oil, it does not yellow with age so much as raw oil, but it does rise in refractive index.

While we have seen the immense care taken by the fourteenth- and fifteenth-century painter in the preparation of the gesso on the panel, it is difficult to get any reliable statement about the preparation of the priming in later centuries. The account given by Vasari is in one place clear, in another quite unintelligible, and later writers on painting, including de Mayern, do not give clear instructions.

Picture restorers have had endless opportunities of finding out the nature of the primings used on canvas, but can give very little information. Generally speaking, we are, I think, justified in assuming that on the whole white lead replaced tempera priming on canvas. The Rokeby Venus was painted on a white lead priming. White lead at its best, when ground in oil, has not the whiteness and power of reflecting light which is possessed by gesso. I am told by restorers that even when painted on canvas, the Dutch little painters used a gesso priming, but there is no definite evidence on this point, and it is quite obvious from the accounts given by de Mayern and by later writers on art, that the importance of a white priming was not realised; consequently, there is that lowering of tone to which I have already referred.

Rembrandt reversed the tradition by starting with a brown and building up to his high lights, but even under his brown priming he had a panel coated with white gesso, so that a certain amount of light was being reflected through his thin brown underpainting. Working up to white lead he lumped it on heavily and used a white lead of very stiff composition. If we come to the Dutch little painters, like Pieter De Hooch, he painted very thinly on a white ground. This is clearly shown in his picture in the National Gallery where the black and white tiles on the floor are showing through the thinly painted dress of the servant maid, owing to the thinness of the painting and the rise of refractive index of the oil. While getting luminosity for the whole picture, by painting thinly on a white ground, his highest lights have been obtained by lumping white lead on the sleeve of the guest, white lead which, when examined under the microscope, is seen to be very coarsely ground and containing dry lumps and particles. The advice given by Rubens to paint whites heavily and to paint thinly in shadows, has been quite misunderstood. I have examined many of his paintings. He starts with a pure white priming, paints thinly upon it so as to get the full value of the reflected white light, but also lumps on white lead for his high lights.

Frequent examples will be found in the pictures of the old masters of the fact that the paint in the darker portions of the picture is laid on more thickly than in the lighter portion, but the significance of this fact does not seem to have been realised. I take as a typical example a portrait of "A Lady" painted about the close of the sixteenth century. I took the trouble to measure the thickness of the paint layer in different portions of this picture, by means of a minute boring instrument. The paint in the dark portions of the picture was from three to four thousandths of an inch in thickness, about the usual thickness of a paint layer laid on by a house-painter, but the flesh painting lying directly on the white gesso was only two or three ten-

H*

thousandths of an inch in thickness, being the thinnest possible glazing of tinted white lead on the gesso below. As the white lead increased in translucency with age, more white light would pass back through the film of paint from the gesso, and any tendency to yellow with age would be corrected by this continuous bleaching process.

Plate 10

PLATE 10   THE ROKEBY VENUS

by Velazquez

National Gallery 2057

120

CHAPTER X

The Rokeby Venus by Velazquez

HAVING discussed very fully the methods of painting used in what I have called the mediæval period, I have chosen the Rokeby Venus as a typical example of the painting of a picture in oil in the seventeenth century.

After the Rokeby Venus was bought by public subscription for the National Gallery, a suffragette slashed the picture with a knife. When I read this in the newspapers, I at once telegraphed to Holroyd and took the first train to London, as it was evident that this would give me the opportunity of making a thorough chemical examination of a picture of that period.

Holroyd allowed me to examine the whole picture with my microscope travelling on a bar, and also gave me some minute scraps of the paint which could not be replaced.

At the time, the genuineness of the picture had been questioned in the Press. One critic said that he had discovered a signature showing it was not by Velazquez. Another critic said that the Cupid was an addition obviously made in the eighteenth century, as the Cupid ribbon was painted with Prussian blue, which was not discovered until the eighteenth century. There was good reason, therefore, for an exhaustive enquiry into the real history of the picture.

The whole picture is painted on a white lead priming. Under the body of Venus the flesh painting is laid on this white lead priming, but in all the rest of the picture the white lead priming had been coated with a red ochre priming, on which all the background is painted.

By adopting this device, Velazquez secured that the flesh of the Venus would always stand out as compared with the background of the picture.

The blue of Cupid's ribbon was made up of a mixture of azurite and smalt. Smalt came into use about 1600, and I have never found azurite on any manuscript or picture after 1650, thus showing that the Cupid was painted before 1650 and, therefore, was part of the original picture.

Just above the waist of the Venus there is a piece of green drapery showing.

The examination of this showed that it was composed of the same blue as the Cupid's ribbon, but owing to a covering of yellow varnish appeared green.

Both azurite and smalt are very weak staining pigments and consequently are affected by the yellow medium. Azurite is therefore condemned as fugitive in the mediæval writings on painting. As an actual fact, azurite itself remains unchanged, and the apparent change is due to the yellowing of the oil.

On examining the flesh I found that white lead had been mixed with a madder lake and a little smalt. This resulted in a very cold flesh tint which I shall discuss later on.

As it had been stated Cupid had been painted in the eighteenth century, I took some photomicrographs of the brushwork of the body of the Cupid and the body of Venus. In both cases, the paint had been laid on in simple straight brushwork, and I found on cutting my bromide print in half and joining the two halves, that the same consistency of white lead and the same brush had been used for painting both, as every little line and stroke of the brush matched in the two photographs. White lead had evidently been ground in oil to a moderate consistency showing the strokes of the brush.

So far then, the picture had been shown to be all painted at the same time and before 1650. It still remained to settle the question whether it was possible to identify it as coming from the studio of Velazquez.

In order to get something thoroughly characteristic of a painter's trade-mark, it is necessary to pick out a place in the picture where he had rapidly dashed in what he wanted. Such a place is found in this picture in the painting of the ribbon on the mirror. I took a photomicrograph of this and a photomicrograph of the tassel on the knee of the Philip, which has also been dashed in with a few free strokes. In cutting the bromide prints in half and joining the edges together, it was obvious that the same hand had painted both. We have, therefore, linked this picture up with the brushwork in a picture which is universally accepted as by Velazquez and demonstrated that the hand that painted the Philip painted the Rokeby Venus.

We have now come to a very interesting question, the fact that the drapery at the waist of the Venus is covered with a yellow varnish which makes it look green, while the ribbon on Cupid painted with the same pigments is blue. On examining the Cupid very carefully through the microscope, I came to the conclusion that a cleaner had, at some date, removed all the old varnish, and had then found the flesh very cold in colour and had glazed thinly with a little lake, leaving the ribbon blue. Having felt that he had over-cleaned the Cupid, he was careful to leave a thin coat of the old varnish on the rest of the picture, thus preventing the flesh of the Venus from looking too cold, and leaving the drapery at the waist of the Venus green instead of blue.

This raised the interesting question whether Velazquez painted the picture with the intention of covering it with a warm-coloured varnish.

The oil varnishes of the seventeenth century, if made from sandarac, would be warm in colour, and the Spanish leather hangings were covered with tin foil and then given their golden hue by varnishing with varnishes into which saffron and aloes had been introduced, so as to give the appearance of gold. I therefore tried an experiment. I got a young artist to paint me a Rokeby Venus using smalt and madder lake. The result was a very cold grey white. I then made up a varnish according to a mediæval recipe for varnishing tin, and laid it over half the picture. The result was a warm and glowing flesh tint.

There has been recently a controversy in the press about the cleaning of certain pictures in the National Gallery, and a similar storm was raised by the artists when the Philip was cleaned. Now we know that the mediæval oil varnishes were warm in colour, and Cennino Cennini specially mentions the change produced in a tempera picture when varnished. Is it not possible that both sides were right in this controversy—the National Gallery picture cleaners were right when they said they had removed nothing but dirty old varnish, and the artists were right because they felt a certain crudity in the clean picture which was due to the fact that when it was painted, the artist knew that the finished product would be covered by a warm coloured varnish?

When the delicate shadows on the body of the Venus are examined under the microscope, they are seen to consist of a translucent brown through which the pigments mixed with the white lead can be seen. These delicate shadows have, I believe, been put in with the finger and not with the brush.

On examining another Velazquez I found that these delicate translucent shadows had been replaced by opaque shadows. Doubtless some restorer in the past had taken off these shadows in cleaning the picture and then replaced them with opaque shadows of his own.

I was consulted about a reputed Velazquez which had suffered at the hands of a picture expert. He had tried to clean the face and had wiped down one side of the face with strong spirits of wine removing all Velazquez's delicate shadows. I advised the making up of a translucent brown matching the brown of the Rokeby Venus, and laying it on very delicately. This treatment was a complete success.

CHAPTER XI

Brushwork

IN the third period after 1550, when the practice of painting in oil had become thoroughly established on modern lines, there is little of interest to be said on this side of the subject, though there are certain questions on which more information would be useful, such as the extent to which the ground on which pictures on canvas were painted was a gesso and not an oil ground. Although hundreds of old pictures have passed through the hands of restorers and the custodians of galleries, this very simple question has never been settled. Vasari gives an account of two methods of preparing canvas, one with a white lead oil priming and the other with a gesso, and oil primings are frequently mentioned by later writers such as de Mayern. In the description I have given of the way in which a typical seventeenth-century picture was painted, taking the Rokeby Venus as my example, we shall find that the canvas was primed with white lead in oil.

The main interest to students of the history of art in this period is the use of the oil medium to introduce a new decorative method by leaving the actual brush strokes visible, and replacing photographic representation by suggestion.

It is very interesting to trace the beginning of this new development during the sixteenth century. It began by painting the highlights with white lead stiffly ground and laid on in relief. The first painter to grasp the full possibilities of showing the brushwork was Titian. This method of painting is fully developed in what is regarded as his last work, "The Crowning with Thorns", in the Munich Pinakothek.

The three great masters of the new technique were Velazquez, Frans Hals and Rembrandt. The study of the actual strokes of the brush as laid on by the master gives us his actual handwriting, in which his own personality and technical skill is expressed. My attention was first directed to this by the late Mr Vicars of Bond Street. We were all engaged in the famous Romney trial and he took me to see a perfect gallery of the English portrait school belonging to a well-known London banker. "We dealers", he told me, "go

by brushwork, that is the artist's true signature which nobody can forge."
Going up to a Reynolds he said, "Do you see how Reynolds has put in that
touch there?" "Now come here and see how Romney does it; this is Gainsborough's touch." After we had studied the English portrait school from this
point of view, I said to him, "I have learnt more from you than from all the
art connoisseurs". He turned to me and said, "My boy, we've *got* to know, we
risk our money on it!"

I then devised for my own use a magnifying camera and took to photographing characteristic brushwork, finding that a magnification of about two
diameters was very suitable for the purpose.

The study of brushwork is not merely the taking of a photograph. You
require several photographs of different pictures by the same master, and to
have strong bromide prints made from the negatives. These should be pinned
on a drawing board and studied from day to day, until the master has told
you all his secrets.

It was my good fortune to be employed by the Duke of Westminster to
take photomicrographs of Rembrandt and his school throughout the galleries
of Europe. For the reader who wishes to make a thorough study of Rembrandt's brushwork I must refer him to my book. I give here one example,
his portrait of "Saskia Laughing", in the Dresden Gallery. It will be noted
that she has some embroidery and little tassels on the shoulder of her dress.
I reproduce the magnified photograph showing how the illusion of these
tassels and embroidery has been produced by means of a most complex and,
to the eye, meaningless series of brush strokes. This brushwork illustrates one
peculiarity which we find throughout his work. He used a white lead of a
remarkable consistency in which he could even model in relief if he wished
to do so. The stiffest ground white lead in oil still flows, but if a little
whitening is worked in with the palette knife, we get white lead of the
Rembrandt quality. Whether this was his secret or not, he never imparted
it to his pupils.

I shall now pass to Frans Hals, who in his own way was also a master of
suggestion but in quite a different way to that used by Rembrandt. We have
in the Edinburgh National Gallery a very interesting picture by Frans Hals.
When purchased it showed a man holding a wine glass in his hand; an engraving existed of a Frans Hals portrait of Verdonck holding the jawbone

of an ass. On cleaning this picture the wine glass disappeared and the jaw-bone was revealed. I give a photomicrograph of the lower part of the face and of one eye, both very characteristic examples of his work.

There is another branch of the subject which has never received the attention it deserves, and that is the painting of foliage, in which each first-class painter has his own style.

I am satisfied from the study of the photomicrographs of Rembrandt and his school, that the Rembrandts in public galleries require the test of the photomicrograph to weed out pictures bearing the Rembrandt signature, which are really painted by one of his school.

The painter of the greatest genius in the Rembrandt school was Carel Fabritius. It is true he died young, but we have hardly anything of his, and the experts are quite willing to pass his pictures as by Rembrandt if they bear a Rembrandt signature.

There is an interesting example of this in the gallery at Cassel. The picture of which I reproduce a photograph was signed Rembrandt and was always accepted by the experts until it was discovered that the Rembrandt signature was a forgery painted over the signature of Fabritius.

Another well-known Rembrandt which is in the Berlin Gallery is, I am satisfied, from the study of the brushwork, by Fabritius.

I suggest a voyage of discovery to some young student with a magnifying camera through the galleries of Europe, but he must be careful to conceal his real object or he will never return alive. I have never forgotten the rage of the Director of a famous Continental Gallery when he thought I was suggesting that one of his pictures was not by Rembrandt. "Nonsense, nonsense" he shouted, "one of the finest Rembrandts in the world". I hurried to explain that I was referring to a Rembrandt in another gallery, he smiled sweetly and said, "You are probably quite right".

The brushwork of the eighteenth-century English School is also well worthy of study by means of photomicrographs.

Plate 11

PLATE II SASKIA LAUGHING

by Rembrandt

Dresden Gallery

Rembrandt Harmensz. van Rijn (1606–1669.) Rembrandt's Gattin Saskia als junges Mädchen. Kgl. Gemäld. Gal. Dresden. N. 1536.

Plate 12

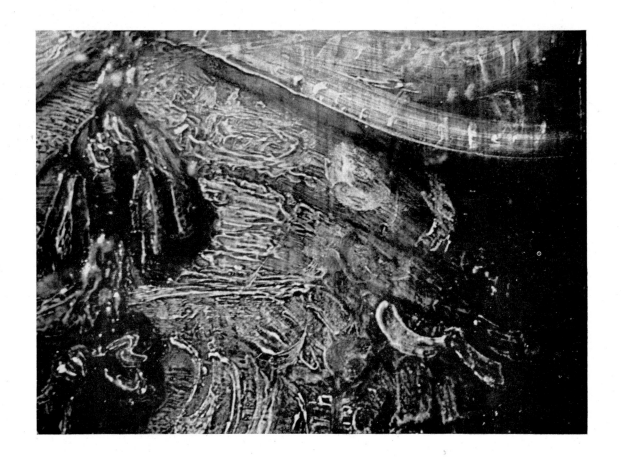

Plate 13

PLATE 13

Photomicrograph of detail from THE RAPE OF PROSERPINE

Kaiser Friedrich Museum, Berlin.   No. 823

I have mentioned in the text the interesting quality of the white lead used by Rembrandt, the secret of which he apparently never revealed to his pupils. This photomicrograph from the PROSERPINE *is of some large leaves in the corner of the picture, and it will be seen that he has used his white lead actually to model the veins of the leaves. I know of only two other instances in which he has done this. The suggestion has been made to me that if a little whitening is worked into a stiffly-ground white lead with the palette knife, it can be used to model on the surface of the picture without flowing.*

Plate 14

PLATE 14

Identifying Rembrandt's brushwork by comparison with brushwork from
WOMAN BATHING

This illustration is a photomicrograph of the highlight on the shoulder of the
WOMAN BATHING, *National Gallery, No. 54. The patch pasted on is
from a photomicrograph of the picture whose attribution had to be tested. It will
be seen that the brushwork is identical in both cases. It is possible for a skilful
forger to imitate a signature, but it is quite impossible to combine the quality of the
paint, the nature of the brush, and the handling of the paint by the painter, so as
to reproduce this complete identity.*

Plate 15

PLATE 15 MAN IN ARMOUR

by Carel Fabritius, with forged Rembrandt signature

Cassel Gallery 245

This picture had on it a Rembrandt signature and was long accepted as a Rembrandt, until a minute examination revealed the Fabritius signature underneath the forged signature of Rembrandt. I have suggested in the text that a careful search through the European galleries with the magnifying camera will reveal other pictures painted by Fabritius, who was the one painter of genius produced in the Rembrandt school. As an example, judging by the brushwork, the SELF PORTRAIT *of Rembrandt in the Kaiser Friedrich Museum No. 810 was painted by Fabritius.*

Plate 16

PLATE 16   SELF-PORTRAIT

Attributed to Rembrandt, signed and dated

Kaiser Friedrich Museum, Berlin, No. 810

Plate 17

PLATE 17   VERDONCK

Portrait of Verdonck holding the jawbone of an ass
by Frans Hals

National Gallery of Scotland, No. 1200

Plate 18

PLATE 18

Brushwork by Frans Hals illustrated by two pictures in the National Gallery of Scotland

Detail from VERDONCK: *Photomicrograph of moustache*

There is a very interesting portrait of Verdonck (No. 1200) holding in his hand the jawbone of an ass. It was known from an engraving that such a picture must have existed, but it had apparently disappeared. The Edinburgh Gallery possessed a picture by Frans Hals of a man holding a wine glass in his hand. An X-ray revealed that underneath the wine glass was the painting of the jawbone of an ass which had been painted out by some restorer and replaced by the wine glass. On careful cleaning, the restorer's work was removed, revealing the lost Frans Hals.

I reproduce photomicrographs of the eye and the moustache from this portrait. These photomicrographs reveal the rapidity with which Frans Hals laid in stroke after stroke with absolute certainty. In fact, the painting seems to be alive, and one can almost see the brush moving over the surface. It would be impossible to mistake this work for the brushwork of Rembrandt which I reproduce on an earlier page.

In addition to these two photomicrographs I reproduce the painting of a hand and the painting of a bow from the other Frans Hals in the Edinburgh Gallery, the PORTRAIT OF A LADY. *It is interesting to compare the painting of this bow with the treatment of a very similar subject in the photomicrograph from Rembrandt's picture* SASKIA LAUGHING.

Plate 19

PLATE 19

Detail from VERDONCK : *photomicrograph of eye*

Plate 20

PLATE 20

Photomicrograph of hand from PORTRAIT OF A LADY *by Frans Hals*

National Gallery of Scotland

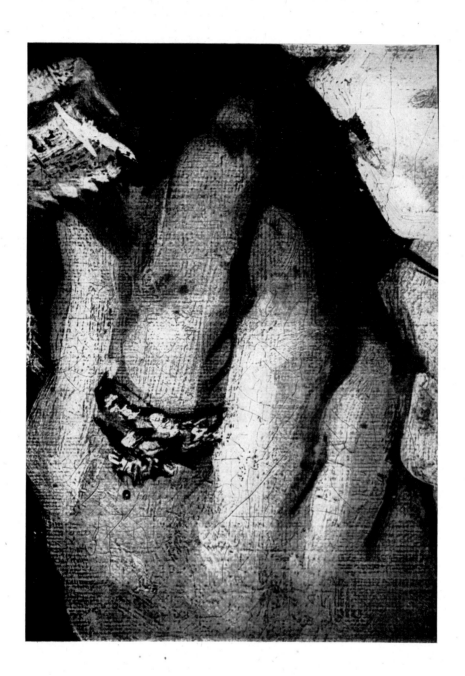

Plate 21

PLATE 2 I

Photomicrograph of bow from
PORTRAIT OF A LADY
by Frans Hals

Plate 22

PLATE 22

THE HONOURABLE MRS GRAHAM
by Thomas Gainsborough

National Gallery of Scotland No. 332

I have suggested in the text that photomicrographs of the English eighteenth-century portrait school would prove most interesting. This and the next photograph are sufficient to suggest how completely these two great painters differed in their handling of the brush.

Plate 23

PLATE 23

LORD NEWTON
by Sir Henry Raeburn

National Gallery of Scotland No. 522

CHAPTER XII

Mediæval Varnishes

ON entering the subject of mediæval varnishes, we find ourselves involved in endless confusion. It has been possible by means of chemical analysis of dated documents to draw up a list of the pigments used, a list which agrees very closely with the pigments given by Cennino Cennini, but it is quite evident that the mediæval painter was not able to distinguish between different resins, and we find in consequence that he probably confused what we call hard resins, such as African copal, with amber, regarding it as a colourless variety. Amber has, of course, been long known, but there is no reason to suppose, when we realise that ultramarine came from central Asia and a dyewood from Ceylon, that mediæval painters were not also familiar with the African copals.

We can divide varnishes into two groups—resins dissolved in linseed oil, and resins dissolved in volatile media like spirits of turpentine and rectified petroleum. The recipes for the "spirit" varnishes are not found till the sixteenth century, which is one of the reasons for supposing that it was not until the close of the fifteenth century that the art of distillation had been sufficiently developed to enable spirits of turpentine and rectified petroleum to become articles of commerce. The first varnishes therefore which we find described are oil varnishes, the resins being dissolved in linseed oil.

Recipes for oil varnishes are given in the Lucca manuscript in which everything soluble or insoluble in linseed oil seems to have been added to the pot. The first recipes we find which are really instructive are two given in the manuscript of Theophilus. He describes first of all the solution of what the varnish maker would call soft resin, and he also gives a recipe for dissolving a hard resin. I quote his two recipes in full.

Chapter XXI. *"Of the varnish gluten."*

"Put linseed oil into a small new pot, and add, very finely powdered, the gum which is called fornis, which has the appearance of the most lucid thus, but, when broken, it yields a brighter lustre. When you have placed this over the fire, cook carefully, so that it may not boil up, until a third part is consumed, and guard

against the flame, because it is very dangerous and is extinguished with difficulty if it be raised. Every painting, covered over with this gluten, is made both beautiful and for ever durable."

Chapter XXII. *"Of the same."*

"Place together four stones which may be able to sustain the fire without flying to pieces, and place a common pot upon them, and put into it the above-mentioned gum fornis, which in Romaic is called glassa, and upon the mouth of this pot place a smaller pot, which has a small hole in the bottom, and lute a paste round it, so that no vapour may come out between these pots. Then place fire carefully underneath, until this gum liquify. You will also have a thin iron rod fitted to a handle, with which you will stir this gum, and with which you can feel when it is quite liquid. Have also a third pot nigh, placed upon the coals, in which is hot linseed oil, and when the gum is quite liquid, so that the iron being extracted a kind of thread is drawn out with it, pour the hot oil into it and stir it with the iron, and thus cook them together that they boil not violently, and at times draw out the iron and daub a little over a piece of wood or stone, to try its substance. And take care in this, that in weight there are two parts of oil and the third part of gum. And when you have carefully cooked it to your wish, removing it from the fire and uncovering it, allow it to cool."

It will be noted that it would be possible to dissolve the soft resin directly in the boiling oil. In the second recipe the resin has to be first fused in the pot and then the hot oil added gradually and the heating continued until a drop of the varnish on being allowed to cool remains clear. Until very recent times, oil varnishes had been made by both these two methods. For instance, if we want to make a varnish out of Sierra Leone copal, it has to be first fused in the pot. The making of varnishes has always been a highly skilled operation and a good varnish maker has always been able to receive a high wage because of his special skill.

Although the resin is partly decomposed by fusion, the resulting varnish is much harder and tougher than one made from a softer resin. The only difference between the recipe given by Theophilus and modern practice, is that a little spirits of turpentine is added to the modern varnish when it is finished. It will be noted that Theophilus distinguishes between the two resins calling one *fornis* and the other *glassa*.

When we come to studying the literature on varnish recipes we find, as

I have said, the greatest confusion. It has been assumed by writers on this subject that *glassa* refers to amber, and we find right through the literature of varnishes, both ancient and modern, recipes for making amber varnish. Eastlake, in his *Materials for a History of Oil Painting*, assumes amber varnishes were used.

I have spent a great deal of time in testing these various recipes. With one exception none of them dissolves amber, and I am satisfied that the various inventors of these recipes assumed that the thickened and darkened linseed oil contained amber. The only recipe that works is to fuse the amber just like the making of a copal varnish, in which case we get a varnish which is so dark as to be useless as a medium for painting, a varnish that will not dry for a very long time, and which has the worst fault that varnish can have, of running down on a surface when it is painted out. I am positive that whatever varnish was used by a mediæval painter, it was not an amber varnish. It is possible to dissolve amber under pressure in chloroform and then mix oil with the solution and distil off the chloroform, but this of course was not known in mediæval times.

When we enquire further we find they had a resin that was called *sandarac* which is not the resin of that name today, but was probably the resin of the juniper, which was apparently imported in large quantities from Africa. It is also called *berenice* and *verenice*, from which the word "varnish" comes, and it is not always clear whether they mean, in the old accounts, the resin or the varnish made from the resin. Professor Church has experimented on this resin, which he finds dissolves in boiling oil, yielding a reddish-brown varnish which must have been allowed for by the painters in tempera and possibly also in oil. In addition to this, they had mastic, which came from the Greek Islands, and is used today as picture varnish, being readily soluble in turpentine, and they had the semi-liquid turpentines from larch and the silver fir. From both of these turpentines it is possible to distil over with the help of steam a spirit of turpentine, leaving a resin behind. These resins from the larch and the silver fir, known as Venice turpentine and Strasbourg turpentine, dissolve readily in oil or in spirits of turpentine, but do not give satisfactory varnishes. We are, therefore, limited to sandarac, mastic and miscellaneous resins which doubtless appeared upon the market, and were assumed to be amber if they were difficult to fuse and to dissolve. There is one other recipe, which we occasionally find, the dissolving of amber in Venice turpentine or resin; it works but does not yield a good varnish.

The recipes for the old varnishes show a very high percentage of resin to oil and according to Cennino Cennini they were warmed and rubbed on with the hand. On the whole they have not proved very durable, having darkened and scaled off the tempera pictures on which they were laid. Varnishes coloured by the adding of aloes were used for the Spanish leather hangings.

Closely connected with this question of picture varnishes is the assumption that the old violins were varnished with a marvellous varnish which has certainly stood the test of time. The Stradivarius varnish is readily soluble in alcohol and I suggest that they were lacquered with shellac.

The magnificent varnish used on coaches and until recently on motor-cars, consisted of an oil copal which was allowed to dry and rubbed down as many as a dozen times for high-class motor-cars.

In the Ely and Westminster accounts varnish is frequently mentioned and it is assumed by Eastlake that because it was sold by the pound it consisted of resin which was dissolved in the oil by the painter. This, I think, is very unlikely, and it is quite clear that Cennino Cennini bought his varnish ready-made from the oil and colourman. We may take it that there is no evidence that mediæval makers of varnish had any secrets or special methods which cannot be reproduced today, and whatever resins they may have used amber was not one of them.

CHAPTER XIII

The Persian Illuminated MSS.

1. THE PIGMENTS

I N order to understand the pigments used in painting the Persian manuscripts, it is necessary to begin by some account of the pigments used for illuminating Western manuscripts.

The Byzantine illuminated manuscripts from the seventh century onwards were painted with orpiment (the native yellow sulphide of arsenic), vermilion, red lead, malachite green, a blue from lapis lazuli, and a purple lake prepared from the murex shellfish.

The vermilion was probably the artificial product, obtained by subliming sulphur and mercury in a closed crucible; but fine samples of the native product, cinnabar, may also have been used. Pliny describes the use of cinnabar, and so it was known in classical times.

The red lead was probably prepared by roasting white lead. The preparation of white lead by the corrosion of lead plates in the presence of the acetic acid vapours from vinegar is described by Pliny, who was familiar also with the yellow pigment, massicot, obtained by roasting lead, and from which red lead can also be prepared by altering the condition of roasting. A very fine orange variety of red lead is obtained by roasting white lead.

Malachite is the native green carbonate of copper.

The blue from lapis lazuli was probably prepared by heating the lapis lazuli and plunging it into water to break it up, grinding, stirring with water, and floating over the blue ultramarine, leaving the other minerals behind. This is a very imperfect method of separating the blue, and accordingly we find the Byzantine blue dull, weak, and revealing under the microscope a large percentage of the other minerals. We shall have to consider a better method of preparation later on, a method which the Byzantine illuminators seem never to have practised. Pliny describes the preparation of a pigment from the murex dye—the famous Tyrian or Imperial purple. Early manuscripts, such as the Carlovingian manuscripts, were frequently painted on parchment dyed with the murex dye, but its use soon disappeared from European manuscripts, with the exception of the Scoto-Irish manuscripts, on which a similar purple was used, prepared from a native shellfish.

The early Persian manuscripts were painted with those pigments. We find them, for example, used in the thirteenth and the fourteenth centuries. Their use seems to have continued to the end of the fourteenth century, after which a change took place. This may possibly have been due to the pigments having been obtained from Byzantium, and that source of supply having been cut off by the advance of the Turks. In the fifteenth century the dull blue is replaced by a very fine ultramarine, and the Tyrian purple pigment is no longer used, but is replaced by mixed tints of mauve and pink.

While on Byzantine manuscripts the ultramarine blue showed no improvement in method of preparation, the preparation of the blue on European manuscripts showed a gradual improvement.

The recipe for preparing a fine blue is a very interesting one in the light of modern methods of ore separation.

The finely powdered lapis lazuli is made into a stiff paste with resin, wax, and linseed oil. This paste is kept for several days, with occasional kneading. It is then pounded in a vessel containing a slightly alkaline solution of warm water, which results in the separation from the mass of a very pure ultramarine blue.

The first appearance I have found of a fine blue is on the Missal of Queen Melissende of Jerusalem, 1131–1144. It is found on Italian manuscripts of 1200, and from that date onwards on European manuscripts. The interesting point to notice is that it does not appear on Persian manuscripts till the fifteenth century, which suggests that although the lapis lazuli was found on the upper waters of the Oxus, the blue was imported from Europe, or the recipe for its manufacture learned in Europe, probably Venice. The fact that it is some two hundred years after its use in Europe that it appears in Persia, suggests a Western recipe. It did not come from China, as I agree with Mr Noel Heaton that the Chinese used azurite.

If we now review the possible sources of supply of pigments in the fifteenth century, we find that Europe could supply real ultramarine, madder lakes and kermes lakes, and possibly white lead and verdigris; India could supply lac lake (the crimson lake extracted from the crude shellac during its purification), Indian yellow or purree, and indigo; China could supply vermilion and Indian ink. In addition, the earth colours, red and yellow ochre, Venetian and Indian red, and hæmatite, would be available, probably from native sources.

While it is impossible to speak with absolute certainty on such a matter without an analysis of many samples, the fifteenth- and sixteenth-century pigments seems to have been—Venetian red, Indian red, vermilion, red lead, yellow ochre, massicot, orpiment, malachite green, real ultramarine, white lead, a black (probably Chinese-Indian ink)—and probably cinnabar, which is a beautiful red, richer than Venetian red. The rich brown of their horses is very nearly matched by hæmatite. The mauve and pink backgrounds can be obtained with real ultramarine and lac lake, or lake from kermes, and vermilion, and white. I doubt if they used verdigris or Indian yellow or indigo.

Indian manuscripts of later date—for example, the poems of Hafiz in the Edinburgh University Library, obviously of Indian origin—show a yellow matching Indian yellow, and mixed greens with yellow and possibly verdigris, and a blue resembling indigo, as well as ultramarine.

The genuine Persian manuscripts of the fifteenth and sixteenth centuries seem to stick closely to one group of pigments, although others must have been available. The greens, though sometimes bright, are always laid on thickly; they are opaque and are apparently always malachite.

The grouping of pigments according to date is no easy matter. In many cases the dates of manuscripts themselves are doubtful; and a later copy would probably require an imitation in tints of the original, and prolonged microscopic and chemical examination would in many cases by necessary to make a distinction.

The following notes on the manuscripts shown at the Persian exhibition (Burlington House, London, 1931) are, therefore, far from complete.

The thirteenth-century manuscripts show the use of a very limited palette. White lead is not used; an undertone of grey is frequent; the blue is always weak; and the vermilion is blue in tint and probably tinted with a crimson lake. It is a tint frequently found on Chinese paintings, a raw liver colour. A pale yellow, probably massicot, is used. Gold leaf is used and very

L

carelessly laid on. An occasional purple lake is seen, probably from murex.

Through the fourteenth century the palette remains very much the same, but becomes a little more elaborate. A typical example is 535B in the catalogue of the Burlington Club's Persian exhibit *Qaz Wim's Cosmography*, which is painted with the badly washed Byzantine blue, vermilion tinted with a crimson lake, red lead, a dull heavy green, probably a poor malachite, and a purple lake, probably the murex dye.

Towards the close of the fourteenth century, I find in my notes occasionally, "blue fairly good", but it is not till the fifteenth century that we get the gorgeous ultramarine of the later manuscripts. A bright green, probably a fine variety of malachite, comes in a little later than the good blue, as I find frequently in my notes, "dull green for the earlier fifteenth-century manuscripts". The use of white lead for whites is also now established, and a full use of earth colours; and a subtle use of reds, from red lead to true vermilion. (I have found the raised white surfaces on an Arabic manuscript to be composed of whitening in place of white lead.) The purple lake of the fourteenth century is no longer seen, but is replaced by mauves made of mixtures of blue and a crimson lake.

This palette seems to remain the same during the fifteenth and sixteenth centuries, reaching its culmination at the close of the fifteenth century. Gold leaf may have been used to cover large surfaces, but a rich red gold paint is almost universal. A poor blue is very rarely seen. Azurite may well have been used in the time of the Mongol conquest, as it is the favourite blue of China; and it is difficult to distinguish merely by inspection a poor ultramarine from a poor azurite. I have identified it on an Arabic *History of the World*, in Edinburgh University Library (20), which was written in 1306 A.D. But if used, it is very rare. According to Percy Brown (*Indian Painting Under the Mughals, A.D. 1750*) azurite was used in Persia in the fifteenth century, and replaced later by lapis lazuli, the azurite coming from a mine in Hungary, in possession of the Turks.

A very fine azurite came into universal use towards the close of the fifteenth century in Europe, and Pacheco (1641) mentions that owing to the conquest of Hungary by the Turks, the azurite, which came from a Hungarian mine, "is getting very rare". It disappeared from the artist's paint box about 1640–1660 in Europe.

Hungary was conquered by the Turks in 1526, so that Percy Brown's statement that owing to this conquest it was used in fifteenth-century manuscripts in Persia is not correct. If the mines were situated in Hungary, it seems much more likely, as its use survived till 1640–1660, that the mine was ultimately exhausted. It is quite possible, of course, that some found its way to Persia, but it is much more likely that any azurite found its way from China, where it was the universal blue used in painting. If used at all, it is very seldom used. Ultramarine from lapis lazuli is the practically universal blue through the fifteenth and sixteenth centuries.

Brown also mentions the use of a lake, prepared from kermes. This is found on the prickly oak all round the Mediterranean, and was used both as a dye and as a lake by European painters, and may well have been used in Persia.

On most of the manuscripts a fine red gold paint is used, and on the very early ones, gold leaf, and possibly on large spaces gold leaf on the later manuscripts. But occasionally this beautiful gold paint, made by grinding gold leaf, is replaced by a dull, heavy, grey gold. The heavy, dull gold paint, where gold leaf has not been used, is very usual on thirteenth- and fourteenth-century manuscripts, but also appears, though rarely, at a later date. I was disposed to assign it as restorer's work, but its appearance on the Arabian manuscript in Edinburgh, already referred to, proves it to have been genuine. Gold dust is sometimes mixed with brown and green pigments, enriching them but being invisible to the eye.

2. THE PAPER

The Persians are believed to have learned the art of making paper from the Chinese. The researches of Wiesner and Karabacek have proved that the Persian paper was a rag paper, made from old linen cloths.

The paper used in the illuminated manuscripts is never white, and is sometimes tinted. It may have discoloured to some extent with age, but the use of white lead for white, and the fact that the light grey of the paper is part of the whole colour scheme, suggests that it must have been originally of the same tint. It could only be sun-bleached; and the whiteness of modern paper, which is far from permanent, is due to powerful chemical bleaching agents.

When examined under the microscope, the Persian paper is seen to consist of long interlocked fibres, much longer and coarser than in modern paper. Today the raw materials of paper are beaten and "cut" in special pulping machines which produce a much finer pulp than Persian paper. My attention was first directed to this by the beauty of their gold paint surfaces. At first I thought the surface had been deliberately scored, but found that the gold lying in the hollows and ridges of the long fibres produced a reticulated surface which brilliantly reflected light. Even a modern water-colour paper cannot produce this effect. It is mechanically uneven but microscopically fine in texture.

The Persian paper has a further advantage of binding the paint much more firmly to the surface.

We have today two kinds of long-fibred paper—blotting paper and filter paper. Blotting paper is too soft, but both white and grey filter paper can be obtained. It should be pasted round the edges to a board, and then sized with a weak solution of the same medium with which the pigments are mixed, to ensure thorough binding of paint to the surface. It could also at this stage be tinted all over.

3. THE MEDIUM

There are several mediums that could have been used—gum arabic, gum tragacanth, gum sarcocolla, glue, starch, and egg.

There is an Egyptian recipe in the Leyden Papyrus (A.D. 400) for a mixture of gum and white of egg; and the Lucca manuscript gives fish glue and gum arabic, and other gums are given by Theophilus and later writers for painting on manuscripts.

We have, therefore, a wide choice, but it is too difficult to obtain a sufficient sample of Persian manuscript painting to decide the question by chemical analysis.

According to M. E. Blochet, author of *Les Origines de la Peinture en Perse*, gum arabic was the medium used, but the medium is too insoluble to be gum arabic alone, while chemical tests show egg or size to be improbable.

The medium must stand a warm, dry atmosphere, and must be sufficiently flexible.

In order to compare these various media, I applied the following tests. I ground zinc white in each of them, and painted each out as a solid coating on blotting paper sized with gum arabic. I also laid on the paper a ridge of paint about a sixteenth of an inch high. The whole was well baked by prolonged drying in front of a gas fire, the ridged portions examined for cracks. The painted out portions were cut out with a knife and the amount of crumbling noticed during cutting, and then they were bent round glass cylinders of 8, 5, and 3 mm. diameter.

Gum arabic alone powders slightly on cutting with the knife and cracks when bent on the 8 mm. cylinder. The ridge of paint cracks badly. A very strong glue, too strong to paint with, does not crack when laid on as a ridge, but powders and scales off when cut with the knife, and cracks on the 8 mm. cylinder. A weak size cracks and powders badly. Yolk of egg powders slightly and only cracks on the 3 mm. cylinder, and cracks slightly when ridged. Gum tragacanth is a very difficult medium to handle. A little added to gum arabic cracks when ridged, powders slightly on cutting, and cracks on the 3 mm. cylinder. It is more elastic, therefore, than pure gum arabic. Gum arabic and white of egg cracks badly when ridged, powders badly, and cracks on the 8 mm. cylinder. Sarcocolla cracks, scales off on cutting with a knife, but does not crack till bent on the 3 mm. cylinder. It is elastic, but does not bind strongly. Of these media the best are egg and gum arabic with a little gum tragacanth added.

These experiments, though capable of much further refinement, give us a rough idea of the properties of these different media.

I then tried some experiments in another direction. I shall presently describe some experiments with Chinese insect wax and beeswax. At present, I wish to describe their properties when added to the medium.

Taking a 10% solution of gum arabic, which is a very convenient strength, I stirred into the boiling liquid 10% of the weight of the gum arabic it contained of Chinese wax, so as to form an emulsion. This emulsion, well shaken, was poured hot on to the muller slab and ground with the pigment. The cooling on the slab and separation of the wax does not matter. A ridge of paint with this medium only shows hair cracks when dried, there is hardly any dust produced when the painted layer is cut with the knife, and it is not cracked even on a cylinder of 3 mm.

L*

Chinese wax is formed on the leaves of certain plants in China by the Coccus ceriferus, and is white, hard, and brittle. It is an article of commerce today, and no doubt would be easily obtained in Persia. Beeswax can be used the same way, but does not grind in properly on the muller, being too soft and sticky. This medium, a gum arabic Chinese wax emulsion, is well worth a trial.

It will be noticed that the surface of the paper of the Persian miniatures, and of the pigments, the white lead especially, has a polished appearance, resembling vellum. It is also remarkable how perfectly the white lead has preserved its white. It has been stated that the paper was burnished with soap, which confirms the view that burnishing was resorted to. It is possible to burnish alone with an agate burnisher, the surface of which is rubbed first on a lump of beeswax, but the process is very tedious. If dipped in hot beeswax it is difficult to distribute evenly. The simplest plan is to cover the surface with finely-powdered Chinese wax, and with a silk rag, to rub gently at first, and then to rub hard. In this way the whole surface, paper and paint, can be covered with a thin protective layer, giving a slight eggshell gloss. This protective layer delays the attack of injurious gases.

It is probable, both from the appearance of the paper when pigment has scaled off, and the uniform glaze over paper and paint, that the burnishing came last. The shiny surface of the paint might be due to excess of gum, but is more likely to be due to a final burnishing with a suitable wax substance.

My suggestions for those who wish to experiment are to obtain from a scientific dealer some sheets of Whatman's white filter paper. Paste round the edges on to a board. Size with a weak solution of gum arabic, mixed with the tinting pigment. Grind the pigments in a medium consisting of 1 oz. gum arabic and 10 oz. water. Chinese wax, 1/10 oz. is then stirred into the boiling liquid, the stirred hot liquid being used as the medium to grind the pigment. This paint mixes with the water and works smoothly under the brush, and can be kept for use after grinding, in a corked bottle.

Paint on genuine gold paint from a shell lightly. One touch of the brush is enough. Burnish the whole surface, paint and paper, with finely-powdered Chinese wax, using a soft rag.

Plate 24

PLATE 24

Travelling microscope on horizontal bar with camera

Up to about 40 diam. diffused daylight near a window is best. If higher powers are needed, with electric light, down the tube of the microscope there is a haze due to reflection from the surface of the oil.

Many years ago Leitz constructed for me a microscope with crossed nicols to remove this reflection. It has now come into universal use.

168

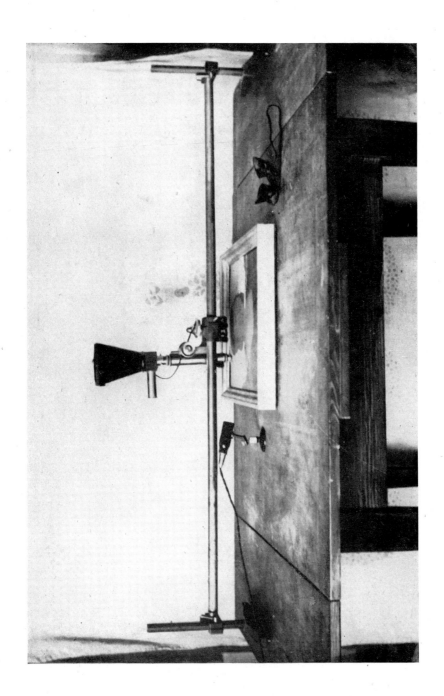

Plate 25

PLATE 25

Ultra-violet Lantern

Plate 26

172

Plate 27

PLATE 27

A forged Hobbema signature

This magnified photograph of a forged signature has an interesting history. I was engaged in taking photomicrographs of the painting of foliage by the landscape painters, and among others had taken a photograph of the foliage of the picture on which this signature appears, and which is an accepted Hobbema. I was satisfied from the photomicrographs of the foliage that the picture had not been painted by Hobbema, and therefore proceeded to examine the signature. It is obvious from the magnified photograph I reproduce that while the forger has been careful to avoid covering some of the larger cracks with his new paint, he has completely smothered the finer cracks in the picture. The "F" and the date evidently belong to the original signature, so there can be no question that the Hobbema signature is a forgery.

CHAPTER XIV

Forgeries

DOUBTLESS from the time that connoisseurs began buying old masters there were forgers and forgeries, but they were on a modest scale, designed to entrap tourists to Italy by selling them a "Botticelli" at a low price, as a bargain.

Today the forgers are assaulting the seats of the mighty, deceiving the "experts" and planting in our public galleries forgeries sold for colossal prices. A few years ago some dealers in Italy employed a young sculptor to make forgeries of the work of the great sculptors of the Renaissance. They were smuggled into the U.S.A. and sold at very high prices to museums and art galleries in America. The forgers had discovered one of the secrets of success, charge a high enough price for your forgery and experts will accept it. When some of the directors of museums wished to make enquiries as to where these statues came from, they were told that a hush-hush policy was necessary, as it was illegal to take works of art from Italy.

Unfortunately, the dealers quarrelled with the sculptor as to the share of the plunder and he was impudent enough to take them into the Law Courts. They were just developing a nice line in classical Greek statues when this exposure took place, and the statues disappeared into the cellars of the galleries and museums. An examination by ultra-violet light would have revealed that the marble was newly cut, and that therefore the statues could not be old. This fraud has recently been followed by an even worse scandal. Vermeer of Delft was not only a great painter, but there are very few of his pictures known, so when a new one was discovered, it fetched a very high price. A few years ago Vermeers began to appear on the market which had never been seen before. They were hailed with enthusiasm by all European experts and sold for enormous prices. A European Gallery paid £100,000 for one of them. A comparatively unknown Dutch painter had painted these brilliant forgeries.

Now one of the difficulties facing the forger is that he can no longer get some of the pigments used in the past, and has to replace them with modern pigments. What are called the dating pigments are known to scientific experts in the history of art. If a chemist had been called in and allowed to take minute samples here and there on the point of a hypodermic needle and submit them to microchemical analysis, the fraud would have been discovered.

When Millet died he left his unsold pictures to his wife and they were subsequently sold by his nephew. They were mentioned by name in the will and when one was sold the French Government supplied a photograph of the entry in the will referring to that picture. It occurred to the nephew that if he employed an artist to paint half a dozen copies of the picture he could sell each of them under the same certificate of the French Government. I remember asking a Custodian of a certain gallery how he knew the picture he had bought was genuine. He replied "We have the certificate of the French Government". It had not occurred to him that the same certificate would do just as well for six pictures as for one, as the French Government supplied them without question. The last time I visited this gallery the picture had disappeared from the wall where it formerly hung.

In the case of a Frans Hals, certified as genuine by a leading Dutch expert, it occurred to someone to take an X-ray of the picture. The old panel which had been used had been strengthened by some battens on the back and they had been nailed on from the front of the panel before the picture was painted, so that the picture was painted over the heads of the nails. The X-ray photograph revealed them to be modern French nails and as their heads lay underneath the paint, it was difficult to see how the paint had been laid on in the time of Frans Hals. In this case the artist who lived by painting Frans Hals forgeries had painted a portrait of himself dressed up in an appropriate costume.

I remember a picture which was hung in the Flemish Exhibition attributed to a well-known old master of the Flemish School. The Hanging Committee found out something suspicious about its history and it disappeared off the line, but it had appeared in the catalogue and was just about to be sold to a U.S.A. collector when it was brought to me.

It is possible to pick up fifteenth-century pictures of little value on a worm-eaten panel and covered with a gesso which has cracked in the most convincing manner. The old paint is removed and the forgery painted on it.

This had been done in the case of this picture. When I examined it under the microscope I said, "This is a forgery". "How do you know?" "The paint has sunk into the cracks."

When the forger was discovered he was asked how it was there were so many repairs on the picture. He replied, "When I have finished a picture I scrape out bits here and there and put in repairs."

There is also the gradual growth of a picture from a fragment as it passes from dealer to dealer. Professor Forbes has an interesting series of photographs illustrating this.

There is in addition the touching up of a battered old master. The ultra-violet light is a deadly weapon for the discovery of such repainting.

Once a London dealer who had his doubts about the touching up of a fifteenth-century landscape, asked me to bring my ultra-violet lantern to examine the picture. The restorer had used chrome yellow both in his greens and his browns. Now chrome yellow is black in ultra-violet light so when I threw a ray from my ultra-violet lantern on it, the picture looked as if someone had splashed it all over with ink.

I remember a judge once asking how much repainting is allowed on an old master for it still to be an old master. "That," replied the expert in the witness box, "is a very difficult question."

I do not know if Ioni is still alive and busy painting fifteenth-century pictures in his tower in Siena, pictures which will ultimately appear in the galleries of American millionaires, or European art galleries, under famous names.

Once he showed a friend of mine who was visiting him his latest triumph. My friend said he was particularly impressed by the carefully repaired crack down the middle of the panel which gave verisimilitude to the whole. "I was looking at it at the open window", said Ioni, "when it slipped from my hands and fell on the pavement below."

This is as good a place as any other to discuss the question of crackle. In a former chapter I stated how panels were covered with gesso. In course of time the gesso shrinks and becomes covered with small cracks like old china. Each little square of gesso is curled up at the edges as a result of the process of shrinking. In the case of forgeries the forger spreads the gesso on a thin piece of canvas on which he paints the picture and then rolls up the picture one way and then again at right angles, so producing a crackle very similar to that seen in an old master. It was pointed out by a connoisseur writing in an art paper that this was easily distinguished from real crackle because the edges were not curled up on the little squares of gesso.

Now there is nothing more dangerous than to have a method of detecting forgeries that cannot be relied on. I therefore decided to see if I could not produce a crackle in which the gesso had curled up at the edges of the squares. If I could do it, the forger could. In the first place, I prepared a gesso containing a little china clay and a little fuller's earth. This gesso dried quite smooth at ordinary temperatures and could then be painted on. On putting it in a hot water oven, it at once became covered with cracks, but these cracks had not the right shape. I therefore took a panel and covered it with a thin coat of gum, cut up some linen sewing thread into short pieces, and with a photograph before me of the crackle on an old picture, picked up the little bits of thread with a pair of pliers and dropped them on the panel in a similar pattern to the old crackle. The whole was then covered with gesso (my particular mixture) allowed to dry, painted on and put in a hot water oven. The cracks now ran along the line of the threads imitating the old crackle perfectly, and the little squares of gesso were curled up at the edges. I chose linen thread because, as the reader will remember, Cennino Cennini used to cover his panels with a piece of old linen before laying on the gesso. If I had used cotton thread and someone had scraped off the gesso and examined the thread under the microscope, my forgery would have been discovered. I had proved that it was possible for an ingenious forger to produce an exact imitation of the old gesso.

The most ingenious forgery I have come across was brought to me to examine by a Director of a Continental gallery. It was a portrait of an old man claiming to be by Rembrandt. I had recently published a book with photomicrographs of Rembrandt's brushwork in his heavy white impasto. The brushwork in the picture exactly corresponded with the brushwork in my book, but the director did not like the picture and brought it to me for further examination. I dug out a little bit of the impasto and found it consisted of plaster of paris with a thin coat of white lead on the top.

Many years ago, reproductions of old masters containing both brushwork and cracks, were produced by photographing a picture, taking a print on sensitive gelatine, developing the gelatine in warm water so as to get the dark portions in relief and the high lights depressed, and then when dry, pressing the print on a gesso still soft and so producing both the brushwork and the cracks; the colouring was then put in by some lithographic process. These were not intended as forgeries, but the forger of this "Rembrandt" had used this process and then painted a "Rembrandt" round the impasto differing slightly from the "Rembrandt" originally photographed. I had been hoist with my own petard.

X-ray photographs revealing under-painting, and ultra-violet light and plates sensitive to infra-red rays, are all useful, but the first step is to examine the picture under a microscope which is mounted on a travelling bar. A magnification of about forty diameters is quite sufficient, the examination being made by daylight close to a window. A wide lens should be used so as to get as much light through as possible. I find the best for my purpose are lenses made by Zeiss. A great deal is learnt by this preliminary examination. The pigments in the old days were ground much coarser than they are today and an old picture looks very like a modern mass of concrete consisting of gravel, cement and sand. Also it is possible to recognise many pigments right away. Charcoal black, azurite mixed with white, and so on. A picture which to the eye has got no cracks, will be found to be covered with minute cracks when examined under the microscope. Consequently all repaints are at once detected as they bridge over these cracks. The skilful repainter may avoid filling up large visible cracks, but is bound to fill up the microscopic cracks.

An old repaint may have also cracked. In such a case, a careful examination will show no continuity between the old cracks and the new. If a signature is examined a forged signature is easily detected. A genuine signature is practically flush with the original painting. A forged signature is not flush and has bridged microscopic cracks. Such forged signatures are very apt to come off when the picture is cleaned. A restorer told me that he always told his pupils to go very lightly over signatures as he would get into trouble with the owner of the picture, if a forged signature had been removed. Pictures in public galleries have been assumed to be Rembrandts because of a Rembrandt signature. The picture is cleaned and the Rembrandt signature comes off revealing the signature of Bol or Flink or Fabritius underneath.

The next step is to remove a minute particle of white lead with a fine hypodermic needle, mount on a slide, dissolve out the white lead with very diluted nitric acid and determine the refractive index of the medium. Care must be taken that it is *old* white lead, not touched up by some former restorer. A tiny particle may also be removed for the purpose of micro-chemical analysis where there is a pigment which it is necessary to identify as either ancient or modern. This minute particle is dissolved in a tiny borax bead. Layer upon layer can be dissolved off this bead with minute drops of water each on a separate slide, so as to carry out a series of chemical tests.

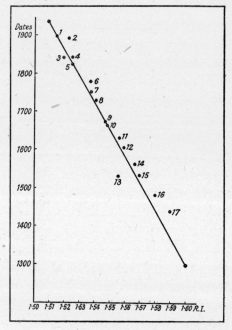

Of course, one has always to look out for new methods of forgery. I remember in one instance a picture on a panel which had no identifying pigments, but I noticed dimly showing, when I examined it under the microscope, a series of criss-cross dark lines lying under the paint

F I G . 4: Graph of the rise in refractive index of linseed oil with time of exposure

surface. On cleaning off the paint on a tiny corner of the panel, I found that a photograph of an engraving had been taken on sensitive gelatine and pressed down on the soft gesso, thus giving a guide to the painter of the picture. The wet paint flowing into these grooves had given the appearance of these dark lines all over the picture.

On one occasion, I found a huge repair on a picture, the gesso of which was covered with crackle. The repairer had painted in by hand the crackle on the repaired portion so perfectly, that it deceived a dealer. The microscope, of course, at once gave it away.

One way or another, a modern scientific examination will result in the discovery of the forgery.

In a former chapter I have dealt very fully with the importance of the study of brushwork by means of photomicrographs to enable us to identify the painter of a particular picture. But there are some cases, especially in the earlier schools of painting, where the brushwork is not shown and we want some more general and reliable tests of authenticity. This can be usually got by a study of the accuracy of the drawing in the picture. It is extraordinary what a difference there is between the drawing of a painter of the first class and a painter of the second class; in fact, I believe that the ultimate classification of painters, although the public are quite unconscious of the fact, depends on the quality of the drawing. Cennino Cennini tells us that you must draw continuously workdays and holidays, and at the end of twelve years, you will be fit to paint pictures.

One of the most interesting cases of a disputed picture that I have come across, was what is known as the Romney trial. A representative of a well-known firm of picture dealers was attending a sale of pictures in a house in the country, pictures which had been collected by the late owner in various places, as examples of the old masters. Among these, was a large picture of two ladies in flowing drapery walking on clouds in the eighteenth-century pseudo-classical manner. It was claimed that the picture had been in the possession of the family for a long time, that it was a portrait of Mrs Siddons and Miss Fanny Kemble and was painted by Sir Joshua Reynolds. The picture was in an eighteenth-century frame and on this frame there was a plaque on which the name of the painter had originally been inscribed. The dealer, catching this plaque in a particular light, saw traces of the name of Romney. He believed he had made a valuable find, bought the picture, and took it to London. He consulted the leading expert on Romney who told him he was satisfied the picture was by Romney, and on looking up Romney's diary in which he entered the names of his sitters, found that at a certain period there appeared, on several occasions, merely the entry "The Ladies". The expert assumed that Romney had asked Mrs Siddons and Miss Fanny Kemble, who were then not so famous as they afterwards became, to pose for him as models, and on the strength of this assumption, he claimed to have discovered the date when the picture had been painted. The picture was sold to Mr Huntington, the well-known American collector, and the dealer was so satisfied of its authenticity that he gave a guarantee. Mr Huntington was advised by the best experts in New York that the picture was not by

Romney, and finally brought it back to England, and brought an action against the dealers for the recovery of the price.

In this case, there was no question of the picture not being a period picture; it was evidently either a picture painted by Romney or by a skilful painter who closely imitated his style.

I determined not only to compare the brushwork with Romney's brushwork, but to compare the accuracy of the drawing with an undoubted Romney. Taking a typical Romney as my example, I posed a model and lighted the face so as to get the lighting the same as in Romney's picture. In order to do this, I took the shadow thrown by the nose on the face as my key shadow. Having taken the photograph and also taken a photograph of the Romney, I compared the photograph of the face in the Romney picture with the photograph of the face of the model. I found that every shadow in Romney's picture had been placed in exactly the right place, showing that Romney had painted the face with the utmost accuracy as far as drawing was concerned. When I applied the same test to the disputed picture, I found the placing of shadows on the face most inaccurate.

Romney was fond of painting ladies standing up and wearing the heavy stiff silks of the period, flowing in folds to their feet. I succeeded in getting hold of some similar silk from Messrs Darling in Princes Street, draped my model in it and photographed the natural folds. On comparing this with the pictures by Romney, I found that he had reproduced most accurately the natural folds taken by the heavy silk under the force of gravity. On now examining the drapery on the disputed picture, I found the most extraordinary errors, the artist having painted the drapery largely out of his head, without observing the model. I was subjected to some criticism by modern artists for this method of testing whether this was Romney's work. Perhaps they were a little nervous about the accuracy of their own drawing. Of course, an artist may choose to leave details undefined and to suggest rather than to copy, or choose to represent human beings like sausages, but behind every line and stroke of the brush, there must be good drawing. We possess in many cases the sketch books of the great artists of the past, and I advise anyone who is aiming at being a painter, to devote more time to the study of these sketch books, than to the study of their finished paintings.

These photographs of mine proved conclusively that Romney could not have painted the disputed picture. In the meantime, fresh evidence was obtained as to the history of the picture, and it was finally proved from documentary evidence which was accepted by the dealers, that the picture had been painted by Josiah Humphrey, a miniature painter, who was a great friend of Romney, and took to portrait painting in his old age, naturally imitating the style of the great master. Now in this trial experts, academicians and others, appeared in the witness box on both sides. Doubtless among experts, and more especially among dealers who risk their money on their judgment, an instinctive knowledge grows up which prevents them in most cases making blunders. But they cannot impart that knowledge. If I state in the witness box that I passed in the street a man with whose face I am familiar and I am asked how I know it was him, I cannot in most cases, answer the question. The same is true about evidence of genuineness of works of art given in the witness box; it is merely a question of opinion against opinion. In this case, our experts were coached on my photographs and the "key shadow of the nose" became a familiar phrase.

To watch Lord Simon cross-examining is a treat for the gods. He is so gentle, so friendly with a hostile witness and then the rapier flashes out and he is pinned. He was our counsel in the famous Romney case. We said the pictures had been painted by Josiah Humphrey and we had a picture of his in Court. It was shown to the "expert" who was giving evidence against us.

Lord Simon: "Are you satisfied the picture in this case is not by Josiah Humphrey?" Witness: "Yes." "Do you know Josiah Humphrey's pictures?" "No." "Your counsel handed you the picture we have in Court. You glanced at it for a few seconds. Is that all you know of his pictures?" "Yes."

Lord Simon left it there, asked some other questions, and then turning up an "Artists' Who's Who" which was on the table, said, "I see you are a famous authority on water colour painting. You have written a book about it." "Yes." "You are an authority on Italian Art, you have written a book about that." The witness looking very pleased, "Yes." You are an authority on the English Portrait School. You have written a book about that." The witness beaming, "Yes." Why had not his own counsel asked him all these nice questions? "And now, Sir, in addition to all that, *You are an authority on Josiah Humphrey*." Collapse of witness and laughter in Court.

In the case of claims to possess valuable pictures, forgeries, as I have said, can be detected, but contemporary pictures by an inferior artist imitating a master, are more difficult to detect. Rival experts will say "yes" or "no" according to the side which is paying their fees. When the painter has a marked and characteristic brushwork, it is easy to detect the work of an imitator by means of a photomicrograph. The imitator either fails to reproduce the brushwork or has to do so by niggly strokes which are revealed by the photomicrograph. Another method which I have found effective is to take full-sized photographs of the faces painted by the master and of a face painted by his imitator, and tell the Jury to look at them upside down. When we look at a face in a portrait, we unconsciously correct bad drawing, but if we turn the face on the photograph upside down, the bad drawing is at once revealed. To draw correctly the human face in oil paint, requires a master of the art. The second rate man is nearly always a bad draughtsman. If he was not, he would probably be regarded as first rate. In a case, for instance, of a picture, claiming to be a Sir Joshua Reynolds, by taking photographs of the face and photographs of a face painted by Sir Joshua and getting Judge, Jury and Counsel to look at these two sets of photographs upside down I convinced them that Sir Joshua had not painted the picture claimed to have been painted by him.

Many years ago, when I was first investigating the pigments, mediums and methods of the painters in the past, a leading picture dealer in Bond Street said to me, "You are wasting your time. If the public believe a picture is by Raphael and will pay the price for a Raphael, then it is a Raphael."

It is time that the public insisted that before pictures are bought for public galleries with *their* money, they are examined by a scientific expert. There is a well-staffed laboratory at the Courtauld Institute and another at the British Museum. There is a famous laboratory in Harvard University, and the National Gallery has a scientific department.

Though it is outside my brief, I cannot resist saying something about frauds on Insurance Companies, in conclusion.

Lloyds insure on your own valuation, so you begin by buying a lot of dud pictures—the cellars of the dealers are full of them—and insure them against fire and burglary at Lloyds for any sum that takes your fancy. I remember a "Gainsborough" insured for £10,000 that had once been pawned for £5. When you have insured them, you arrange a fire or burglary and claim your money. Then the trouble begins, but Lloyds will always rather compromise than have a fight in the Law Courts.

Be careful that your pictures are completely burnt, and that your burglar destroys his loot, lest they turn up in Court to your confusion.

I remember one case where some pictures were not completely burnt. Among them was a small panel picture of an old man called a "Rembrandt" and insured for £4,000. The fire had not injured it, but there was a broad scratch right down the middle of the face, supposed to have happened in the haste of removal. I examined the scratch under the microscope, and saw a series of shallow parallel grooves on the gesso uncovered by the scratch. What could they be? They were the marks left by the milled edge of a coin. The edge of a shilling had been pressed into the picture and then torn down the face, thus turning a worthless picture into £4,000. That one little mistake proved unfortunate when assessing the claim for damage.

In the eighteenth century there was an ingenious method, before lithography was invented, of copying pictures by stencilling through silk.

The pictures of a certain popular painter of the eighteenth century had been reproduced several times in this way, and one of these copies was posing as an original among other pictures that had been recovered after a burglary, by an ingenious gentleman who makes a liaison between burglars and Insurance Companies, and recovers stolen articles for a price.

Sir Charles Holmes at once recognised the picture as one of these copies, and hunting round among dealers, had picked up five more. The "expert" for the victim of the burglary said it was an original worth £1,000. We produced one of the other copies. "Another original" he said, "the artist had painted a replica, then three, then four, then five, then six. They were all originals", he shouted, "well worth £1,000 each."

The most difficult case I ever had was one of the owner of a "Vandyck", who had the fire insurance extended to wherever the picture might be. The picture, we were told, was packed in a case, tied to the back of a motor-car and the motor-car had caught fire and destroyed the picture. Nothing was left except a few fragments of the packing case, the plaque on the picture, a few pieces of charred canvas, and the ashes below, where the picture had been burnt. These ashes we carefully collected.

After a long investigation, I succeeded in proving that only the frame of the picture and a few pieces of canvas had been put in the case, which had then been packed full of fireworks so as to ensure a thorough burning.

CHAPTER XV

Emulsions and the Van Eyck Medium

WE ARE all familiar with the fact that by dissolving in water substances like gum and size, we can get two immiscibles like oil and water to mix and remain mixed for some time. Such emulsions are the basis of many water paints used for distempering walls, and are preferred as more durable and washable than size distemper. The question as to how far such emulsions were used is of importance to the student of the history of painting, and to the painter of today.

One emulsion of oil and water and albumen was long used as a painter's medium, namely yolk of egg, and it has stood well the test of time. But it is not capable of being reproduced by shaking up oil and the white of an egg, because it contains a third substance, an emulsifying agent, lecithin. Of recent years much attention has been bestowed on emulsifying agents which will bind the water solution and the oil together. Such bodies consist of molecules with different chemical properties at the two ends, like the north and south poles of a magnet, thus forming a connecting link. The yolk of egg is therefore a very perfect emulsion. In time the albumen becomes insoluble, the oil oxidises, and the blend produces a very durable film.

The fifteenth-century painter had at his command the yolk and the white of an egg, linseed and nut oil, oleo-resins like Venice turpentine, resins like mastic, and sandarac, gums soluble in water, glue, and flour paste. He knew how to thicken oil so as to make what is called a stand oil, to prepare boiled and quick-drying oils, and to make oil varnishes. I can find no indication that oil of turpentine, or spike oil, or a rectified petroleum was used in the first half of the fifteenth century. The preparation of these required a knowledge of the art of distillation, an art known to the alchemists from the second century of our era, but apparently not commercially used until the distillation of wine to produce brandy had become a common practice.

It is obvious that, from the list I have given above, many mixtures could be made and must have been tried. It is possible, for example, to convert a sticky stand oil, copal varnish, or Venice turpentine into a slick medium with a little white or yolk of egg. If, beginning with the egg yolk, we add linseed oil drop by drop, we obtain at first a medium which still can be mixed with water. As we add more, we obtain a medium mixing with difficulty with both water and turpentine. A further addition of oil gives a medium which will only mix with turpentine. We have passed from a watery emulsion containing oil to an oil emulsion containing water. The addition of a little oil to egg yields a more flexible medium, the use of which is suggested by the appearance of some paintings of the late fifteenth and early sixteenth centuries. The addition of a little egg to white lead in oil gives a paint which can be laid and modelled in sharp ridges without flowing.

The fifteenth-century oil and tempera painters must have been quite familiar with these facts, and the next question we have to ask is whether their use was an established painting practice. Were the pictures of the fifteenth, sixteenth, and seventeenth centuries painted with an emulsion? Microchemical analysis of tiny particles of pictures is advancing from the identification of pigments to the identification of media. Mr G. L. Stout of the Fogg Art Museum has made a thorough investigation of the differential straining of such emulsions. While awaiting more definite information from chemists, it remains for us to examine the evidence from manuscripts and other writings containing painting recipes.

I know of only four such references: one in the Hermeneia, and one in the Le Begue manuscript, both of which refer to emulsions containing wax and wood ashes; one in the Bolognese manuscript where instructions are given to grind lake in oil and white of egg; and one in the Venetian manuscript, quoted by Ernst Berger, for using a mixture of egg and varnish to paint on glass. Against this very scanty evidence, we have the definite statement by Vasari that egg-oil emulsions had been tried by Alesso Baldovinetti, Pesello, and others and had failed. And it is remarkable that the physician, de Mayerne, who was interested in the materials used in painting, and was in close conversation with the painters of his time, like Van Dyck, in all his innumerable recipes, never suggests the use of an emulsion. On the other hand, there are innumerable recipes for the preparation of oils and the grinding of colours in them, and Vasari himself tells us quite definitely that pigments are ground in linseed or nut oil, and that this is their tempera or medium. The whole evidence both positive and negative from literary sources is against the use of anything but oil, with the possible addition of a little varnish.

On the other hand, it is obvious that the early oil pictures have been painted with something different to the ordinary oil medium, and I believe I was the first to suggest the possibility of an emulsion afterwards developed more fully by Professor Berger in his *Maltechnik*. This was before I had studied the technique of the sign writers, so completely different to that of the ordinary painter in oil, and necessitating the use of a thick, sticky medium like Stand Oil. Once the technique of the sign writers is understood, the information on oil painting given by Cennino Cennini becomes intelligible. The absence of any description of an emulsion, the deliberate thickening of the raw oil and the use of a miniver brush are all explained.

It is some years since I first published in *Technical Studies* my identification of the Van Eyck medium. It has not received much attention because the connoisseur and the painter have not taken the trouble to study the technique of the sign writers, a small group of highly trained craftsmen who have handed down through the centuries the technique of the early oil painters. The identification of the Van Eyck medium completes our knowledge of the methods and materials used by the medieval painter.

There is no need to invent imaginary media, or assume unrevealed secrets. Let a plain tale suffice.

INDEX

Aëtius   Page 87
Aidan, Saint   53
Alcherius   61
Amatisto   63–66
Amber   157
Arzica   63, 68
Augustine, Saint   53
Auripigmentum   67
Azurite   55
Azzuro della Magna   70–71
Barbara, Santa   104
Bellini, Giovanni   105
Berger, Ernst   19
Biacca   69–70
Bianco Sangiovanni   69
Bice, blue and green   56, 74
Breughel, Pieter   97–98
Black pigments   63
Brixillium   59
Buon fresco   35–47
Cennino Cennini   17, 42–47, 50, 63–74, 93–94, 103
Chinese Wax   165
Church, Prof. on Mediaeval varnishes   79
Cima da Conegliano   103–104
Cinnabar   63
Clothlet tints   50
Coccus Ilicis   59
Cochineal   59
Columba, Saint   53
Coram Rege rolls   52
Crimson Lake   59
Crivelli   105
Didron   41
Diversarum Artium Schedula   14, 88–89, 155–156
Dragon's blood   63, 66–67
Dyes, classical period   27–28

Eastlake   Page 19, 96
— oil in tempera pictures   90
Edgar, King   56
Egg, yolk   82–83
Egyptian pigments   23
— method of preparing surface for painting   23
Egyptian blue   24–25
Ely and Westminster accounts   90
Emulsion, recipes for   187–189
Eraclius   89–90
Eyck, Jan van   87, 96–97, 104, 189
— signature   95
Fabritius, Carel   126
Fornis   156
Fresco, account by Vitruvius   36–40
— experiments on marble and plaster   36–40
Ganosis   40
Gesso grosso   81
— sottile   81
Gettins, R. T.   18
Giallorino   63, 67
Glassa   156–157
Glue   80–81
Gold dust   56
Gold, mordants for   82
Gypsum, Egyptian use of   35
Hals, Frans   125–127
Hawara, wax portraits   29, 31
Heaton, Noel   36
Hermeneia, fresco painting   41
Herringham, Lady   79, 80
Ink   102
Iona   53
Juniper, resin varnish   79
Kermes   59
Knossos frescoes   36
Lac Lake   59

Lakes	Page 55–61, 74	Sign-writers' brushes		95
Lamp black	63	Sinopia		63
Lapis Lazuli	55	Speculum Vitae Christi		61, 99
Larch	157	Spike oil		98
Lindisfarne	53–54	Smalt		74
Lucca MS.	19, 87	Stand oil		94
MACLEHOSE, LOUISA S.	18	Stout, G. T.		18
Madder lake	58–61	Strasbourg turpentine		157
Malachite	52, 53, 63	TEMPERA SOCIETY		19
Mastic	157, 187	Theophilus (see Diversarum)		
Melissenda, Queen	55	— varnish recipes	155–156	
Merrifield, Mrs	19	Thompson, Daniel V.		18
Michelangelo	103–104	Titian		125
Minium	66	Turpentine		98
Mount Athos	41	Tyrian purple		52–54
Murex	28, 52	ULTRAMARINE	55, 71–73	
OCHRE, YELLOW	63, 67	VARNISH on Tempera		80
Orpiment	53, 63, 67	— on Egyptian coffins		23
PAPYRUS PAPER	25	Vasari		17
Pentimenta	116	— on technique		18
Petroleum	98	Vegetable pigments		49
Persian pigments	159–163	Velazquez	121–124	
— paper	163–164	Venice turpentine		157
— medium	164–166	Verderame		63, 69
Pezzuole	50	Verde terra		63, 69
Pliny	26–28	Verde azzuro		63
Photomicrography	125–127	Verdigris	56, 63, 69	
Prussian blue	75	Verditer (blue and green bice)		
Purpura capillus	53		56, 74	
RAPHAEL	105	Verdonck	126–127	
Red lead	52, 53, 66	Vermilion	51, 64–65	
Rembrandt	117, 125–127	Verzino		59
Resinate of copper	57–58	Vitruvius on fresco		36–39
Risalgallo	63, 68	WAX, used as a painting		
Rokeby Venus	121–124	medium		29–33
Rubens	117	Westminster, Duke of	19, 126	
SANDARAC	157	Westminster and Ely accounts		90
Sap green	57	White of Egg		23
Schedula (see Diversarum)		Wilfrid, Saint		53
Silver fir	157	ZAFFERANO		63